Arithmetic Enrichment ~~Activities~~

for

Elementary School Children

A collection of practical classroom procedures and activities for the enrichment of arithmetic teaching.

ARITHMETIC ENRICHMENT

Parker
Publishing
Company, Inc.
West Nyack, New York

Joseph Crescimbeni, Ph. D.
Associate Professor, and Director
of Graduate Elementary Education
Jacksonville University

ACTIVITIES FOR

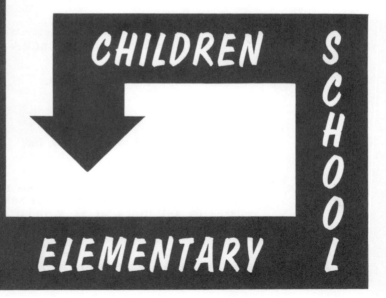

CHILDREN SCHOOL

ELEMENTARY

Seventh Printing.....February, 1969

Arithmetic Enrichment Activities
For Elementary School Children
by
Joseph Crescimbeni

© 1965 by

Parker Publishing Company, Inc.

West Nyack, N.Y.

LIBRARY OF CONGRESS
CATALOG CARD NUMBER: 65–17811

PRINTED IN THE UNITED STATES OF AMERICA
04617—B&P

Dedicated to

John and Jayne

Acknowledgments

The author is indebted to the many students in his University classes who contributed ideas and suggestions used in this manuscript. He also wishes to thank Benjamin Westbrock for his guidance in its preparation, and Angela Holland for the competent typing and proofreading.

Special thanks are accorded to Geoffrey Skog who coordinated the art work along with the valuable help of Mary Bowe, Victoria Pratt, and Kathleen Wood—all art education students at the University of Bridgeport.

To the Teacher:

Learning can be fun. Arithmetic teaching can be learning *and* fun! Here is a collection of enrichment aids to assist you. Use them as before-school exercises, as part of the formal arithmetic period, as game activities during inclement weather recess periods, or concomitant learning activities.

Instructional materials used in the elementary school classrooms have undergone radical changes in the past few years. Yet, regardless of the types or kinds of materials that are developed for basic curriculum instruction, enrichment aids are necessary as supplemental and motivational learning devices for children.

If arithmetic teaching is to be socially vital and practical for all children, then many forms of sensory aids must be used as frequently as possible. Teachers must recognize that utilization of sensory aids assists the child to visualize the relationships involved in a particular problem situation, and this acts as an incentive to learning by appealing to as many of his senses as possible. A child who learns the "laws of arithmetic" by making, manipulating, and discovering how these laws are related and how their relationships change, on a learning device, is far richer in experience than the child who has been subjected solely to the formal introduction of the laws on the chalkboard.

This handbook constitutes a basic attempt at presenting a variety of enrichment activities that can be used with children in all phases of arithmetical understanding. Such sensory aids include brain teasers, learning devices, games, puzzles, manipulative equipment, and bulletin board stimulation. They are *not* a solution for mathematical problems, but rather another method of showing how arithmetic is functional and related to our daily activities. These devices must be used illustratively, carefully, and purposefully. They should relieve the feeling of boredom and apathy that may befall children during the memorization-rote phase of mathematical study. Their specific purpose is not only to make arithmetic more interesting, but to allow children to engage in experiences which stimulate curiosity and understanding.

Sensory aids are related to four specific goals in the teaching of mathematics: (1) they build fundamental concepts of mathematics; (2) they assist to reintroduce the fundamental processes and operations; (3) they make arithmetic teaching more interesting and stimulating; and (4) they tend to motivate intensive study of number operations.

Joseph Crescimbeni

CONTENTS

PART ONE

BRAIN TEASERS 19

Marble Balance	[4–6] .	21
Proving Your Age	[4–6] .	22
Number Is Always 10,890	[4–6] .	22
Multiplying by 9	[4–6] .	23
Number Is Always 5	[4–6] .	23
The Number Is Always 9	[4–6] .	24
Reversing a Number	[4–6] .	24
The Number Is Always 15	[4–6] .	24
Number Is Always 7	[4–6] .	25
Crossing Out to Find a Sum	[4–6] .	25
Answer Is Always 2	[4–6] .	26
Guessing Numbers	[4–6] .	26
A Riddle Poem	[4–6] .	27
Guessing a Number	[4–6] .	27
Three Digit Rapid Multiplication . . .	[4–6] .	28
How Many Trains?	[4–6] .	28
100 Items, 100 Cents	[4–6] .	29
Guessing Your Age and House Number . .	[4–6] .	30
The Persistent Snail	[4–6] .	30
Order of 9's	[4–6] .	30
Magic Addition	[4–6] .	30
The Horse Trader	[4–6] .	31
The Milk Problem	[4–6] .	31
Rapid Multiplication	[4–6] .	32
I Can Guess Your Age	[4–6] .	32
The Freight Train	[5–6] .	33
Secret Code	[5–6] .	34
A Novel Method of Multiplication . . .	[4–6] .	35
Find the Squares	[4–6] .	35
Trick Questions	[3–6] .	36
Rules for Rapid Multiplication and Division		37

PART TWO

LEARNING DEVICES 41

Electrical Wizard . . . . [K–2] . 43
Number Family Addition . . . . . . [K–2] . 44
The Bird Game . . . . [K–2] . 45
Take a Number . . . . [K–2] . 47
Surprise Dots . . . . [K–2] . 47
Guessing at Fractions . . . . [K–2] . 47
Making a Store . . . . [K–2] . 49
Domino Cards . . . . [K–2] . 50
Recognizing Fractional Parts . . . . . [K–2] . 51
Clothespin Counter . . . . [K–2] . 52
A Peg Board . . . . [K–2] . 53
Balance . . . . [K–2] . 54
Egg Box Pitch . . . . [K–2] . 55
Number Box . . . . [K–2] . 56
Race . . . . [2–4] . 57
The Same Sum Number . . . . [2–4] . 58
Seven Sequence . . . . [2–4] . 59
A Secret Message . . . . [2–4] . 60
In Round Figures . . . . [2–4] . 60
Illustration Board . . . . [2–4] . 61
February Picture Puzzle . . . . [2–4] . 62
Matho . . . . [2–4] . 64
The Leaf Game . . . . [2–4] . 65
Wheel Multiplication . . . . [2–4] . 65
Making a Slide Rule . . . . [2–4] . 65
The Twenty Stick . . . . [K–2] . 68
Cardboard Strip Reckoner . . . . . . [K–2] . 68
How Many Squares? . . . . [2–6] . 69
Learning Odd Numbers . . . . [2–3] . 69
Missing Fact Cards . . . . [2–4] . 70
Circle of Facts . . . . [2–5] . 70
Lotto . . . . [2–4] . 71
Card Matching . . . . [2–4] . 72
The Double Chart . . . . [2–4] . 73
Number Combination Cards . . . . . [2–4] . 74
Single Line Abacus . . . . [K–2] . 74
Materials for Teaching Fractions . . . . [2–4] . 75

The Beanbag Game . . . . [2–4] . 76
Playing Fireman . . . . [2–3] . 77
A Magic Rectangle . . . . [2–4] . 78
A Magic Circle . . . . [2–4] . 78
Measurement Equivalents . . . . . [3–4] . 79
Directional Puzzle . . . . [3–4] . 80
A Treasure Hunt . . . . [3–4] . 80
The Adjustable Thermometer . . . . . [3–4] . 81
Flexible Hundred Board . . . . . . [3–4] . 82
Crossword Puzzles . . . . [3–6] . 83
Wheel Game . . . . [2–6] . 85
Discovering Numbers . . . . [2–6] . 85
Using the Number Line . . . . . . [2–6] . 86
Learning Terms . . . . [4–6] . 86
Abbreviations . . . . [4–6] . 87
Numberland Game . . . . [4–6] . 87
Finding Arithmetic Pairs . . . . . . [4–6] . 89
Football Game . . . . [4–6] . 89
Map Treasure Hunt . . . . [4–6] . 90
The Satellite Game . . . . [4–6] . 92
I'm Thinking Again . . . . [4–6] . 93
Upside-down Magic Square . . . . . [4–6] . 93
Raceway Game . . . . [4–6] . 94
Decimal Relay . . . . [4–6] . 94
Lattice Multiplication . . . . [4–6] . 95
Problem Lattice Multiplication . . . . [4–6] . 95
Baseball . . . . [4–6] . 96
The Magic Star . . . . [5–6] . 97
Discovering a Sum . . . . [4–6] . 98
The Flannel Board . . . . [K–6] . 99
Place Value Chart . . . . [K–6] . 99

PART THREE

GAMES 103

Arranging or Ordering Numbers . . . . [K–2] . 105
Bouncing the Ball . . . . [K–2] . 105
Buzz-Buzz . . . . [K–2] . 105
Fox and Chickens . . . . [K–2] . 106
I Can Match That Number . . . . . . [K–2] . 106
I Have That Number . . . . [K–2] . 106

Matching Cards . . . . [K–2] . 107
Lotto . . . . [K–2] . 107
Number Guessing Game . . . . [K–2] . 107
Postman . . . . [K–2] . 108
Tens and Ones . . . . [K–2] . 108
Arabic Number . . . . [K–2] . 108
Scramble . . . . [K–2] . 109
Number Party . . . . [K–2] . 109
Basketball . . . . [K–2] . 109
Pegs . . . . [K–2] . 110
Ten Little Indians . . . . [K–2] . 110
The Train . . . . [K–2] . 110
As I Remember . . . . [K–2] . 111
Baseball . . . . [K–2] . 111
Bean Bag . . . . [K–2] . 111
Breaking Through the Lines . . . . . . [K–2] . 112
I Bought . . . . [K–2] . 112
Christmas Stocking . . . . [K–2] . 112
Climb the Ladder . . . . [K–2] . 113
Combination Solitaire . . . . [K–2] . 113
Dog and His Bone . . . . [K–2] . 114
Finding a Number . . . . [K–2] . 114
Fish Pond . . . . [K–2] . 114
Fox and Geese . . . . [K–2] . 115
Gathering Acorns . . . . [K–2] . 115
Guess What It Is . . . . [K–2] . 116
Hide and Say . . . . [K–2] . 116
Hopscotch . . . . [K–2] . 116
Horse Race . . . . [K–2] . 117
Hull Gull . . . . [K–2] . 117
King of the Castle . . . . [K–2] . 118
Larks, Robins, and Swallows . . . . . [K–2] . 118
Making a Tree . . . . [K–2] . 119
More or Less . . . . [K–2] . 119
Racing: Two by Two . . . . [K–2] . 119
Ring Toss . . . . [K–2] . 120
Numbo . . . . [K–2] . 120
Opposites and Answers . . . . [K–2] . 120
Pairs . . . . [2–3] . 121
Kitten in the Corner . . . . [2–3] . 122
Pony Track . . . . [2–3] . 122
Relay Race . . . . [2–3] . 122
Sorting Mail . . . . [2–3] . 123

The Valentine Box . . . . [2–3] . 123
What Number? . . . . [2–3] . 123
The Teacher . . . . [2–3] . 124
Zooks . . . . [2–3] . 124
An Arithmetic Bee . . . . [2–3] . 125
Baseball Game . . . . [2–3] . 125
Checkers . . . . [2–3] . 125
Factoring Practice . . . . [2–3] . 126
Simon Says . . . . [2–3] . 126
Silent Multiplication . . . . [3–4] . 127
Stepping Stones . . . . [2–3] . 127
Telephone . . . . [2–3] . 128
Twenty Questions . . . . [2–3] . 128
Footprints . . . . [2–3] . 128
Call and Catch . . . . [2–3] . 129
Arithmetic Tag . . . . [2–3] . 129
Ruler Relay . . . . [2–4] . 130
Circle the Clock . . . . [2–4] . 131
Guess What I Am . . . . [2–4] . 131
Ladder . . . . [3–6] . 132
The Whole Story . . . . [3–4] . 132
Bowling . . . . [3–4] . 133
Paper Relay . . . . [3–4] . 133
Tick-Tack-Toe . . . . [3–4] . 134
The Traveler . . . . [3–4] . 134
Around the Circle . . . . [3–4] . 134
Improved Baseball . . . . [4–6] . 135
Bank For Me . . . . [4–6] . 135
Step Up . . . . [4–6] . 136
Multiplication Relay . . . . [4–6] . 136
Golf . . . . [4–6] . 137
Divide It . . . . [4–6] . 137
How Much? . . . . [4–6] . 137
Television Quiz Show . . . . . . [4–6] . 138
Time Around the World . . . . . . [4–6] . 139
Addition Relay . . . . [4–6] . 139
Division Tables . . . . [4–6] . 140
Caller . . . . [4–6] . 141
Math-tic . . . . [4–6] . 142
Fraction Change . . . . [4–6] . 143
Estimation . . . . [4–6] . 144
Containers . . . . [4–6] . 144
Measure in Place . . . . [4–6] . 144

Decimal Point . . . . [4–6] . 145
Bridging Numbers . . . . [4–6] . 145
Teams . . . . [4–6] . 145
Guess . . . . [4–6] . 146
The Domino Sums . . . . [4–6] . 147
Captains Compete . . . . [4–6] . 147
Store Sales . . . . [4–6] . 147
Division Steps . . . . [4–6] . 148
I'm Thinking (2) . . . . [4–6] . 148
Fraction Relay Race . . . . [4–6] . 149

PART FOUR

PUZZLES 151

The Hidden Animal . . . . [K–2] . 153
What Comes Next? . . . . [2–4] . 154
Fruit Puzzle . . . . [2–4] . 155
Octopus . . . . [2–4] . 156
How Many? . . . . [2–4] . 157
Add-a-Trail . . . . [2–4] . 157
Fill in Missing Numbers . . . . [2–4] . 158
Measurements . . . . [4–6] . 158
Mental Arithmetic . . . . [4–6] . 158
Magic Wheel . . . . [2–4] . 159
Magic Star . . . . [2–4] . 159
Number Fun With Circles . . . . . . [2–4] . 160
Puzzle Matching . . . . [2–4] . 161
Discovering Order of Numbers . . . . . [2–4] . 162
Magic Squares . . . . [2–6] . 163
Choose a Favorite Number . . . . . . [2–6] . 164
The Funny 9 . . . . [3–6] . 164
I Can Read Your Mind . . . . [2–6] . 165
The Answer is Always the Same . . . . [2–6] . 165
Find the Mystery Number . . . . . . [2–6] . 165
Number Code Puzzle . . . . [4–6] . 166
Multiplication Crossword Puzzle . . . . [4–6] . 166
Crossword Puzzle . . . . [4–6] . 168
A Surprise . . . . [4–6] . 169
Casting Out Nines . . . . [4–6] . 169
Strange Patterns in Multiplication . . . . [4–6] . 170
Working With 8's . . . . [4–6] . 170

Working With 4's . . . . [4–6] . 171
Products of One . . . . [4–6] . 171
An Arithmetic Crossword Puzzle . . . . [4–6] . 171
Thinking Crossword . . . . [4–6] . 172
Fish Weight . . . . [4–6] . 173
Fill In Number . . . . [4–6] . 173
Finding the Missing Numerals . . . . . [4–6] . 174
Puzzle Matching Numbers . . . . . . [2–4] . 174
A Coded Letter . . . . [4–6] . 175
Discovering Numbers . . . . [4–6] . 176
Fill in the Missing Numbers . . . . . . [4–6] . 176
Placing Numerals . . . . [4–6] . 177
Why We Invert . . . . [5–6] . 179
Working With Different Bases 180

PART FIVE

EQUIPMENT 183

Useful Classroom Materials for Teaching Arithmetic . . 185
Commercial Companies Offering Arithmetical
    Enrichment Aids for Teachers 187
Free Monthly Arithmetic Publications
    Available to Teachers 188
Educational Journals Containing Practical Teaching
    Aids and Articles in Arithmetic 189
Teacher's Directory of Information for New
    Math Programs 191
Commercial Arithmetic Games That Can Be Used
    in the Classroom 192

PART SIX

BULLETIN BOARDS 201

INDEX 216

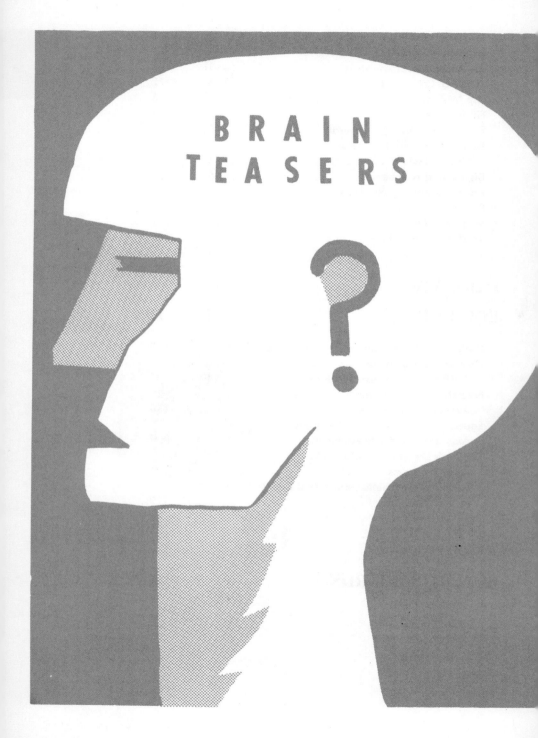

Children like to tackle what often appears as impossible. Brain teasers, or problem solving questions as they are sometimes called, afford them this opportunity. No doubt, many youngsters have difficulty in understanding what is required in a brain teaser, especially if it is a "trick question" type. But, doing one or two examples with the class initially helps set the stage for this type of mental activity.

Brain teasers can be used as a "quieting down exercise" just before the formal lesson in arithmetic, or they can be used as a before-school activity. Many teachers like to give this type of activity as a "homework problem," so that children will share it with their parents and thereby actively involve them in their arithmetical learnings and understandings.

The brain teaser activity should not be restricted to the bright student, as has often been the practice, but rather it should be given to the whole class. Many creative children who do not register an especially high degree of intelligence often find the answers to brain teasers faster than the identified intelligent student. Brain teasers should be an activity that is open to all the students of your classroom.

PART ONE

BRAIN TEASERS

Here are nine marbles, all of which are the same size, color and shape. Eight of the marbles are the same in weight. One marble weighs *less* than the others. Using the balance scale only *twice,* how would you find out which marble is lighter?

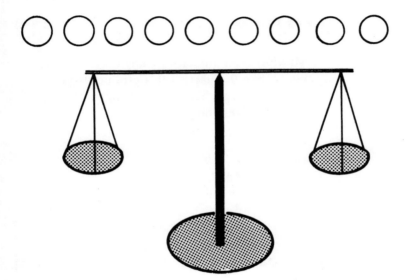

Solution:

Divide the marbles into three groups of three. Keep one group in your hand, and put the other two groups on the scale. If the scale balances, you know the lighter marble is in the group in your hand. If the scale does not balance, you will be able to see which group on the scale has the lighter marble. Thus, in the first weighing, you will eliminate six marbles and have three marbles left— one of which is the lighter marble.

Of these three marbles, put two on the scale and keep one in your hand. If the scale balances, you have the lighter marble in your hand. If the scale does not balance, you can see which side of the scale has the lighter marble.

Proving Your Age [4–6]

Multiply the number 9 by any other number lower than 9. Subtract this product from 10 times your age. The first two digits plus the last digit gives you your age.

Example:
$$9 \times 6 = 54$$
$$10 \times 30 \text{ (age)} = 300$$
$$300 - 54 = 246$$
$$24 + 6 = 30 \text{ (your age)}$$

Number Is Always 10,890 [4–6]

Write four of the larger digits in descending sequence.
Reverse the order and subtract.
Reverse again and add.
The result is *always 10,890.*

Example:

$$
\begin{array}{r}
8765 \\
-\ 5678 \\
\hline
3087 \\
+\ 7803 \\
\hline
10,890
\end{array}
$$

Multiplying by 9   [4–6]

Multiply any number by 9. The sum of the digits in the answer is *invariably 9,* or *9 times a number*.

Example:

$$15 \times 9 = 135$$
$$1 + 3 + 5 = 9$$

Number Is Always 5   [4–6]

Write any number. Add the next highest number.
Add 9 to the sum.
Divide by 2 and subtract the original number.
The result is *always 5*.

Example:

$$5 + 6 = 11$$
$$11 + 9 = 20$$
$$20 \div 2 = 10$$
$$10 - 5 = 5$$

Think of a number.
Multiply it by 2.
Add 18 to the product.
Divide by 2.
Subtract the original number.
The result is *always 9*.

Example:

$$7 \text{ (number chosen)} \times 2 = 14$$
$$14 + 18 = 32$$
$$32 \div 2 = 16$$
$$16 - 7 = 9$$

Reversing a Number   [4–6]

Take any number, reverse it, then subtract.
The remainder will be *exactly divisible by 9*.

Example:

$$16 \text{ (number chosen)}$$
$$61 \text{ (reversed)}$$
$$\overline{}$$
$$61 - 16 = 45$$
$$45 \text{ is divisible by } 9 = 5$$

The Number Is Always 15   [4–6]

Think of a number and multiply by 5.
To the product add 25.
Divide the sum by 5.
Subtract the number you started with.
Multiply the remainder by 3.
The final product is always 15.

Example:

$$7 \text{ (number chosen)} \times 5 = 35$$
$$35 + 25 = 60$$
$$60 \div 5 = 12$$
$$12 - 7 = 5$$
$$5 \times 3 = 15$$

Number Is Always 7 [4–6]

Think of a number 1 through 8.
Add 9 to the chosen number.
Double the sum.
Subtract 4.
Divide by 2.
Subtract the number chosen.
The number is *always 7*.

Example:

$$7 \text{ (number chosen)} + 9 = 16$$
$$16 \times 2 = 32$$
$$32 - 4 = 28$$
$$28 \div 2 = 14$$
$$14 - 7 = 7$$

Crossing Out to Find a Sum [4–6]

Erase six of the nine figures in the numbers listed so that the remaining three figures have a sum of 20.

$$999$$
$$777$$
$$\underline{111}$$

Answer:

Cross out all the 7's.
Cross out two 9's.
Cross out one 1.
This leaves $11 + 9 = 20$

Think of any number 1 through 9.
Add 1 and multiply by 3.
Add 2 and multiply by 4.
Add 1 and divide by 3.
Add 1 and divide by 4.
Subtract your original number.
The answer is *always 2*.

Example:

8 (number chosen) $+ 1 \times 3 = 27$
$27 + 2 \times 4 = 116$
$116 + 1 \div 3 = 39$
$39 + 1 \div 4 = 10$
$10 - 8 = 2$

Guessing Numbers [4–6]

Have the children choose any number from
4 through 9.
Multiply the number chosen by 6.
Add 12 to the product.
Divide the sum by 2.
Have the children tell you their answer.
You can tell them their favorite number.

Answer:
Divide the number given by 3 and subtract
2 from the quotient.

Example:

7 is the number chosen.
$7 \times 6 = 42$
$42 + 12 = 54$
$54 \div 2 = 27$
$27 \div 3 = 9$
$9 - 2 = 7$ (the original number)

A Riddle Poem [4–6]

Try this riddle poem:

"Twice eight and five crows sitting in the rain.
One shot killed a seventh.
How many did remain?"

Answer:
$$\text{Twice } 8 = 16 + 5 = 21$$
$$\tfrac{1}{7} \text{ of } 21 = 3$$
3 crows (dead) remained.

Guessing a Number [4–6]

Tell your class to pick any number, 1 through 8.
Multiply the number by 3.
Add 1 to the product.
Multiply the sum by 3.
Add 8 to the product.
The answer is the tens figure of the sum.

Example:

$$
\begin{array}{r}
7 \text{ (number chosen)} \\
\times\ 3 \\
\hline
21 \\
+\ 1 \\
\hline
22 \\
\times\ 3 \\
\hline
66 \\
+\ 8 \\
\hline
71
\end{array}
$$

Answer:

7 (tens figure of sum)

Tell your class this problem. Have one child write any combination of three digits on the board. Repeat the operation two additional times. You can then add two other sets of three digits and give him the sum immediately.

Example:

                643 (child's number)
                724 (child's number)
                835 (child's number)
                356 (your number)
          + 275 (your number)

Answer: 2833

Explanation:

1. You obtain the first row of digits you write by subtracting each digit of the first number from 9.
   6 4 3—first row (child's)
   3 5 6—fourth row (yours)

2. The fifth row is obtained by subtracting each digit of the second number from 9.
   7 2 4—second row (child's)
   2 7 5—fifth row (yours)

3. Add 2000 to the third row and subtract 2.

How Many Trains? [4–6]

Every hour, and on the hour, a train leaves New York City for Philadelphia, while another train leaves Philadelphia for New York City. The trip between the two cities takes exactly two hours. How many of the trains going in the opposite direction will the New York train to Philadelphia meet?

Answer:

 5 trains

Explanation:

 You leave New York at 8:00 a.m., and you meet one train coming in from Philadelphia.

 You arrive in Philadelphia at 10:00 a.m. and you meet the last train from Philadelphia.

 Now, you have also met the other trains that left Philadelphia in between and they are:

The 6:00 a.m. train	first train
The 7:00 a.m. train	second train
The 8:00 a.m. train	third train
The 9:00 a.m. train	fourth train
The 10:00 a.m. train	fifth train

100 Items, 100 Cents   [4–6]

Susan was given a dollar to buy some school supplies for the opening day of school. She went to the store and found that pencils cost 10¢ each, erasers cost 5¢ each, and paper clips were two for 1¢.

She bought 100 things. What did she buy?

Answer:

 90 paper clips, 9 erasers, and 1 pencil

Guessing Your Age and House Number [4–6]

Take your house number and double it. Add 5. Multiply by 50. Add your age. Add 365. Subtract 615. The last two digits are your age. The other digits are your house number.

The Persistent Snail [4–6]

A snail climbs up a fence 20 feet high, five feet every day, and slips down four feet every night. At this rate, how long will it take the snail to reach the top?

Answer:
16 days. He gains one foot every day for 15 days. On the 16th day he climbs over the top.

Order of 9's [4–6]

Can you write four 9's so that they equal 100?

Answer:
$$99\% = 100$$

Magic Addition [4–6]

Arrange the numerals 1 through 9 in such a way that the sum is 100.

Answer:

$$47$$
$$15$$
$$36$$
$$\overline{98}$$
$$2$$
$$\overline{100}$$

The Horse Trader [4–6]

A man bought a horse for $90.00. He later sold it for $100.00. Still later, he bought the same horse back for $80.00. Did he lose money or make money on the horse trade?

Answer:
He made money. His profit was $20.00.

The Milk Problem [4–6]

A farmer has an eight gallon tank of milk. He wants to divide it equally between two people, but he has only an empty five gallon tank and a three gallon tank to measure with. How does he solve this problem?

Answer:
He fills the five gallon tank from the eight gallon tank. He then fills the three from the five. He pours the three into the eight, puts the two from the five into the three, and then fills the five out of the eight. Then from the five he fills the three.

1. Multiplication of any two numbers between 10 and 20 can be done quickly without writing them down.

Example:

$$12 \times 18$$

First step: $12 + 8 = 20$ (tens)
Second step: $2 \times 8 = 16$ (ones)

20 tens (200) + 16 ones (16) = 216

Example:

$$15 \times 19$$

First step: $15 + 9 = 24$ (tens)
Second step: $5 \times 9 = 45$ (ones)

24 tens (240) + 45 ones (45) = 285

2. Multiplication of two numbers of two figures of which the tens are the same (mental arithmetic).

Example:

$$46 \times 49$$

First step: $46 + 9 = 55$ (tens)
$55 \times 4 = 220$ (tens)
$6 \times 9 = 54$ (ones)

220 (tens) + 54 (ones) = 2,254

I Can Guess Your Age

Here are six sets of numbers. There are three columns in each set. To find out a person's age, ask him to show you which sets of numbers contain his age.

Solution:
Add the upper left-hand figure in the sets he chose and you will have the correct answer.

8	27	46		1	23	45		16	27	54
9	28	47		3	25	47		17	28	55
10	29	56		5	27	49		18	29	56
11	30	57		7	29	51		19	30	57
12	31	58		9	31	53		20	31	58
13	40	59		11	33	55		21	48	59
14	41	60		13	35	57		22	49	60
15	42	61		15	37	59		23	50	61
24	43	62		17	39	61		24	51	62
25	44	63		19	41	63		25	52	63
26	45			21	43			26	53	

4	23	46		32	43	54		2	23	46
5	28	47		33	44	55		3	26	47
6	29	52		34	45	56		6	27	50
7	30	53		35	46	57		7	30	51
12	31	54		36	47	58		10	31	54
13	36	55		37	48	59		11	34	55
14	37	60		38	49	60		14	35	58
15	38	61		39	50	61		15	38	59
20	39	62		40	51	62		18	39	62
21	44	63		41	52	63		19	42	63
22	45			42	53			22	43	

The Freight Train   **[5–6]**

A freight train one mile long is about to enter a tunnel that is one mile long. If the train is traveling at a speed of 15 miles per hour, how long does it take the train to pass through the mile-long tunnel?

Answer:
8 minutes

Explanation:

As the train first enters the tunnel, the whole mile length of the train is still out of the tunnel. After it goes one mile, the front end of the train comes out of the tunnel, but the whole length of the train is still in the tunnel. After it travels a second mile, the rear end of the train comes out of the tunnel. So it takes the distance of two miles to pass through and out of the tunnel.

The train is going at 15 miles per hour.

15 miles into 60 minutes is 1 mile every 4 minutes.

We agree the train went two miles.

2 miles $\times$ 4 minutes = 8 minutes.

Secret Code   [5–6]

Solve the following examples. Then look at the code key on the opposite page. Put the letter which corresponds to the number in your answer into the column at the right. Read the message.

$6 + 7 + 1 \div 2 =$ $6 \times 3 + 2 =$
$10 + 10 - 5 =$ $2 \times 2 + 4 =$
$7 + 9 - 1 =$ $3 \times 4 \times 0 + 9 =$
$7 + 9 \div 4 =$ $6 \times 5 - 15 + 4 =$
$8 + 6 \div 7 =$ $6 + 6 + 8 - 1 =$
$3 + 2 \times 5 =$ $5 \times 3 + 5 + 1 =$
$4 + 3 \times 5 \div 7 =$ $7 \times 4 - 15 =$
$2 \times 4 \div 2 \times 2 =$ $8 \times 3 - 11 =$
$9 \times 9 - 80 =$ $5 + 10 \div 3 =$
$6 \times 2 + 10 =$ $2 \times 5 + 8 =$
$9 \times 5 - 5 \div 8 =$
$8 \times 6 \div 2 \div 4 =$
$3 \times 4 + 9 =$
$5 \times 2 + 4 =$

Key

A = 1	F = 6	K = 11	P = 16	U = 21
B = 2	G = 7	L = 12	Q = 17	V = 22
C = 3	H = 8	M = 13	R = 18	W = 23
D = 4	I = 9	N = 14	S = 19	X = 24
E = 5	J = 10	O = 15	T = 20	Y = 25
		Z = 26		

Answer: GOODBYE, HAVE FUN THIS SUMMER

A Novel Method of Multiplication [4–6]

Take any two numbers .... 68 × 26

Take ½ of the first number
Double the second .... 34 × 52

Continue until you have
1 in the first column ...... 17 × 104

(Drop all fractions)   8 × 208
                                2 × 832
                                1 × 1664

Finally, add all the numbers
in the second column that are
opposite the odd numbers in
the first column   104
                             + 1664
                    Answer: 1768

Find the Squares [4–6]

How many squares can you find in the design at the top of the next page?

15 is considered good. 17 is very good. If you found 20—you were excellent.

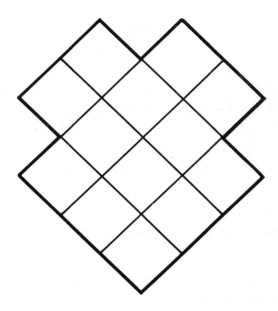

Trick Questions

The teacher can add fun and humor to any classroom situation by asking trick or non-sense questions. This type of question builds perceptive acuity, however, and is a good way to begin a formal math lesson.

1. What has three feet and cannot walk?
   Answer: A yardstick

2. What are two fours?
   Answer: 44 or 8 (depending on the pupil's answer)

3. Robert has two coins which total 60 cents. One of the coins is *not* a dime. What are the coins?
   Answer: A half dollar and a dime. One of the coins (the half dollar) is not a dime.

4. What numeral can be written three times so that the sum is 24?

> *Answer:* $8 + 8 + 8 = 24$ or
> $22 + 2 = 24$

5. A farmer has two haystacks in a large field. On the other side of the field are 5½ more haystacks. If he decides to put them all together, how many haystacks does he have?
   Answer: One large haystack.

6. Let's multiply this number.
   $6 \times 3 \times 2 \times 0 \times 3 \times 1.$
   Answer: zero

Rules for Rapid Multiplication and Division

Multiplying a number by 5:	Take half of the number and multiply by 10.
Multiplying a number by 15:	Multiply the number by 10 and add half the number to it.
Multiplying by 9:	Multiply the number by 10 and subtract the number from it.
Dividing by 5:	Multiply the number by 2 and divide by 10.
Dividing by 15:	Multiply the number by 2 and divide by 30.
Multiplying by 99: ...	Multiply the number by 100 and subtract from this product the original number.
Multiplying by any multiple of 9:	Round the number to the nearest whole number. Multiply your number by this

and subtract one tenth of the product from the product.

Multiplying by 2½: . . Multiply half the number by 5.

Multiplying by ¾: . . . Take half the number and add to it half of the half.

Multiplying by 18: . . . Multiply the number by 20 and subtract one-tenth of this product from the original product.

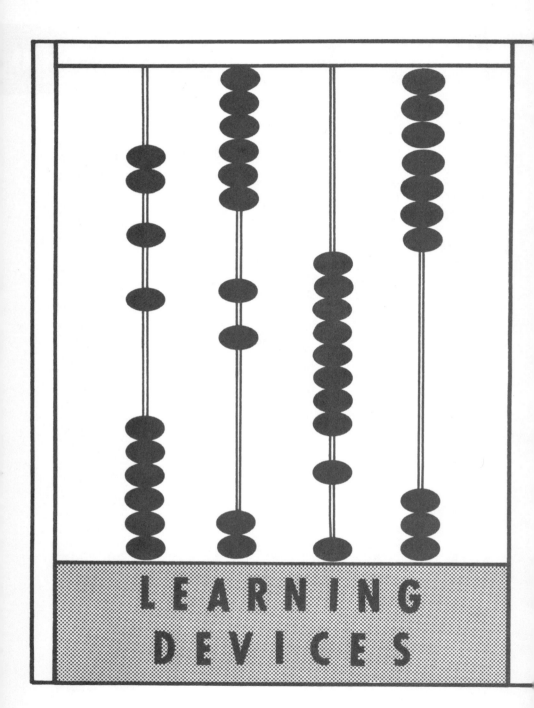

LEARNING DEVICES

Learning devices should be placed in a corner of the classroom where they can be available to all the children. Perhaps they can be packaged and stored in a specific envelope and listed under a file system. Many teachers place four or five learning devices, applicable to the arithmetical concept being taught, on a corner table and allow the children freedom in their usage. Certainly the number line, the counting frame, the abacus and the place value chart should have continual exposure to youngsters.

Most teachers find that children are naturally curious, and the opportunity of having learning devices available and accessible to them stimulates their attitude of inquiry even more.

Learning devices can also become a classroom project in that children should be allowed to help make these devices. Often the purpose of the learning device is more understood through its construction, as well as through its application. Learning devices should be used frequently, and more than one learning device should be utilized for the teaching of any one particular concept. Varied application of learning devices for understanding a number operation strengthens the operational principle of that number concept, and allows the children to experience an "over-all" view of that principle or concept.

PART TWO

LEARNING DEVICES

This game can be purchased commercially, but why not have your students assist in its construction?

Obtain a large board to which file cards (3″ × 5″) may be tacked in two vertical columns of 10 cards each. Install

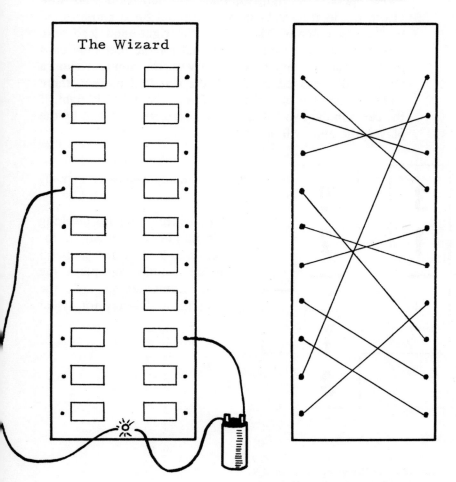

The Wizard

terminals along the side of the board as shown below. Attach the indicated socket and flashlight bulb. Wire the "Wizard" on the back of the board. Make the lead wires long enough to reach the topmost terminals easily.

Make one set of 10 cards with dot pictures for the numerals 1 through 10 in standard patterns, one to a card. Tack these cards in random order in a column opposite the left-hand terminals. Make another set of 10 cards on which are written the numerals 1 through 10. Tack these cards in a column opposite the right-hand terminals. The position of each card in the second column, in relation to its matching card in the first column, is determined by the wiring diagram shown on the previous page.

To operate the Wizard, place the left-hand lead wire (from the light socket) on the terminal for a chosen card in the first column. Then place the right-hand lead wire (from the dry cell) on the terminal for the matching card in the other column. If the card with the numeral chosen matches the selected card with the standard pattern, there will be a complete electrical circuit and the bulb will light. If the cards in the two columns are incorrectly matched by the player, the bulb will not light.

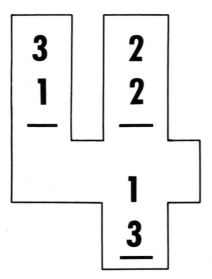

Number Family Addition   [K–2]

Use this technique for teaching simple number computations for numerals 1–9. Cut the numeral from the oaktag and place the various combinations of the number on it. Display for visual reference.

Take a ride with the bird as it loops through the air by writing the answer to each addition example.

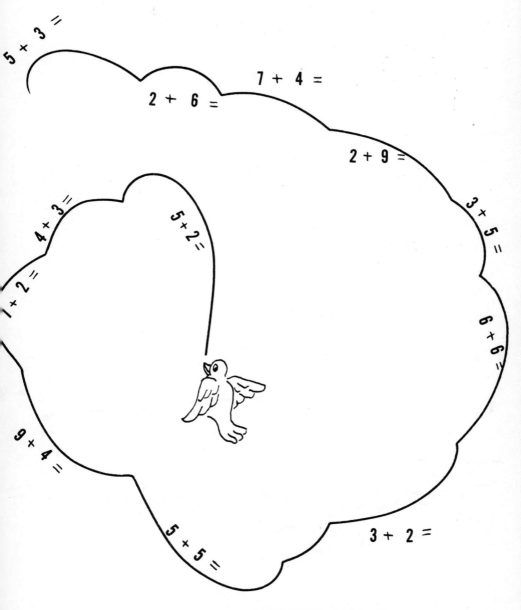

5 + 3 =

2 + 6 =

7 + 4 =

2 + 9 =

3 + 5 =

4 + 3 =

5 + 2 =

1 + 2 =

6 + 6 =

9 + 4 =

5 + 5 =

3 + 2 =

6 •

• 10

7 •

8
•

4 •

9
•

5 •————————————————————• 1

• 3

2 •

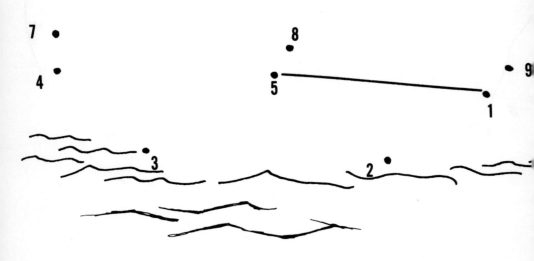

Take a Number [K–2]

Duplicate sets of cards are made containing cardinal numbers on one side and ordinal numbers on the other (one number to a card, as 2 and second). Write four cardinal numbers on the chalkboard. Select four cards and duplicates that match the numbers on the board. Give the eight cards to pupils, who are seated in two rows of four seats each at right angles to the board. A ninth pupil stands between the two rows, as IT, and points to one of the four cardinal numbers on the board. If he calls out "two," the pupil in each row who has the corresponding card looks for the other pupil and attempts to exchange seats with him. IT tries to get one of the seats. If he succeeds, the slow player forfeits his card and becomes IT.

Have at least 28 cards in the cardinal set, printing all to 20, and continuing with tens, as 30, 40, to 100.

Surprise Dots [K–2]

Connect the numbered dots with straight lines. What have you drawn?

The teacher and the children should create other designs using this procedure.

Guessing at Fractions [K–2]

Write yes or no in the blanks on page 48.

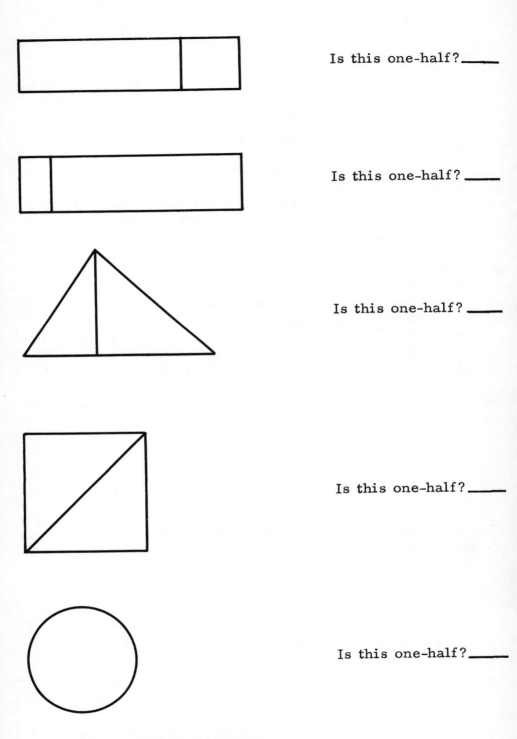

Is this one-half?_____

Is this one-half?_____

Is this one-half?_____

Is this one-half?_____

Is this one-half?_____

48 ■ *LEARNING DEVICES*

One of the most useful devices, particularly in teaching money problems, is the "play store." Pupils have inevitably indulged in this activity at home, and will be ready to offer assistance in preparing materials for this experience.

Obtain any large box, open at the front. Place various objects, with clearly marked prices, within the store. Use a toy cash register to record sales. Use toy or real money to determine expenditures and change.

Domino cards, as well as wooden dominoes, can be used successfully for teaching addition facts, subtraction facts and the laws of arithmetic.

Obtain strong cardboard and cut out to a 4″ × 8″ size for each domino. Use a felt marker pen to establish the numerical patterns. Keep them handy for before-school activities or supplemental lesson teaching.

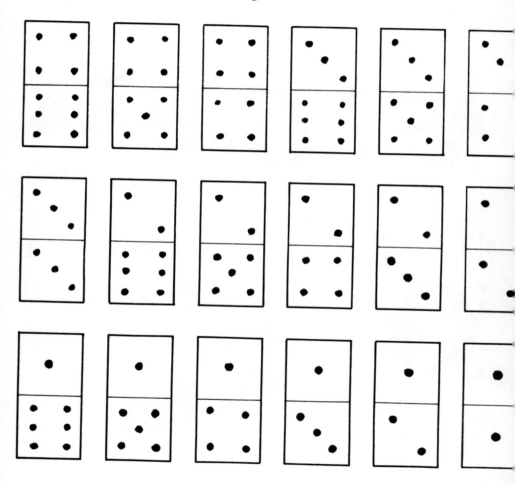

A.   Put a cross (X) in half of the circles.

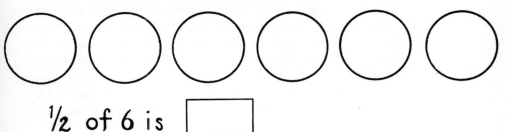

½ of 6 is ☐

B.   Put a line under one-fourth of the triangles.

C.   Divide this set of stars into two equal subsets.

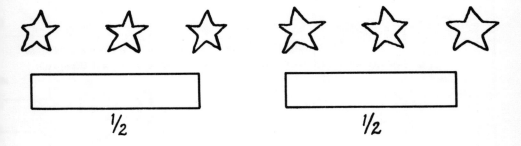

½   ½

D.   Divide this set of stickmen into three equal subsets.

A clothespin counter can be made by obtaining a strong wire coat hanger. The hanger should be painted a bright color to attract attention to its usefulness. Then get spring-type clothespins, and paint each set of 10 a different color. Cards with numerals may be attached to the clothespins if desired.

This teaching aid is useful for teaching counting 1–10, and then 11–20, and the teaching of meaning and symbols for these numbers.

By using clothespins of different colors, experiences may be provided which will relate to discovering or verifying component parts of groups, as well as addition and subtraction facts.

A similar teaching aid may also be made from this same basic idea but using drapery hooks instead of clothespins.

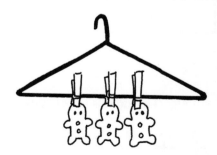

Hang special objects that are familiar to children, or objects that can lead to motivation and stimulation to precede a teaching concept or operation.

A Peg Board [K–2]

Obtain a piece of acoustical tile or a piece of Masonite board with drilled holes, cut in such a way that there will be 10 rows of holes with 10 holes in each row. Gather 100 kindergarten pegs for use with the board. Dowel rods or candy sticks can also be used.

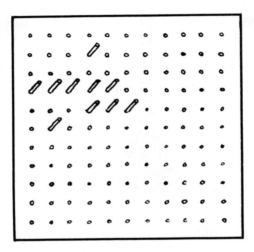

Children may use the board to show standard patterns for groups as large as 10, or to show patterned arrangements for such groups. By grouping and regrouping pegs, childen may discover or verify component parts of groups, addition facts, and subtraction facts.

This activity is designed mainly for addition and subtraction, and is designed to facilitate learning of simple facts.

Obtain or construct a balance scale. Obtain 18 small blocks of wood that are identical in weight.

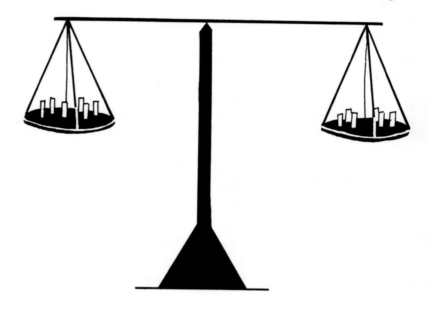

Divide the class into teams and start the game by placing a number of blocks on one tray of the balance and a lesser number of blocks on the other tray. Teams take turns telling the number of blocks needed to make the scale balance evenly.

Give points for correct answer. If both students fail to guess the right answer, the opposing teams each lose points.

Change the block combinations and alternate from one team to another. The team with the most points at the end of the game wins.

All you need is an empty egg box with sectioning in it. Cut off the top cover and with crayon write a number on each egg wall section. Smear paste along the inside bottom and sides of the box. Place the sectioning rack back into the box, and when the paste dries, the rack will be held in place.

Each player takes a turn throwing three buttons into the box from behind a line six feet away. A player must then add up the numbers indicated on the egg wall sections. He can use paper if he wants to. If he misses, he should add a zero for a number.

There are many variations for this game; for instance, the player who scores twenty-one first is the winner. Each time he answers correctly he gets a point.

Provide a series of number boxes for each child in the classroom. Children can bring in empty candy boxes or cigar boxes to store materials. Boxes should be painted attractively and bear the child's name. The box should contain approximately 20 small objects that can be used as counters and that can be manipulated easily. Checkers, buttons, bottle caps, and small cubes are examples of counting material. Play material should also include small counting sticks, play money, tongue depressers, and similar objects.

As a motivational factor a mystery box can be passed out to each student prior to an arithmetic lesson. The box may contain a numerical concept or operation, such as $14 + 7 - 3 + 8$. The child would then use the number counters in the box to determine the answer. This could be done before school or during the formal teaching lesson.

Uses: The playingboard for this game contains questions which must be answered by the pupils. Variation may therefore be obtained by changing the playingboard. For example: the board shown below might have combinations for a single process, rather than mixed combinations for the four processes. The squares could also ask children to read abstract numbers or give correct fractional answers, depending on the grades.

Preparation: Use 9″ × 12″ construction paper and mark off 20 rectangles (more or less if desired). Reserve a few rectangles in which directions may be written, and write Multiplication, Addition, Division, and Subtraction (MADS) combinations in others. Make a spinner with numbers from one to four. As a substitute, use small cards numbered from one to four. Obtain counters, or have the children make them.

START	$6 + 7$	$11 - 5$	Forgot something go back to start	$5 + 6$
Red Light lose 1 turn	$3 + 8$	$8 + 3$	Downhill ahead	Shortcut go to $5 + 2$
$9 \div 3$	Uphill back 1	No gas back 3	$12 - 7$	$8 + 5$
Number Land	$3 + 7$	$5 + 2$	Super Highway 1 extra turn	$9 + 8$

Directions: Take turns spinning or drawing cards to discover the number of spaces to advance. If the incorrect answer is given, the pupils may receive help. In this case, though, his marker stays in the square just as though he had answered correctly, but when his turn comes to advance again, he may not, until he can give the correct answer for the square he missed previously. The first player to reach NUMBERLAND is the winner.

The Same Sum Number [2–4]

Find one number that will fit in the corners of the puzzle so that each side will add up to a total of 21. Use the *same* number in all four corners.

	5	4	
8			2
1			7
	9	0	

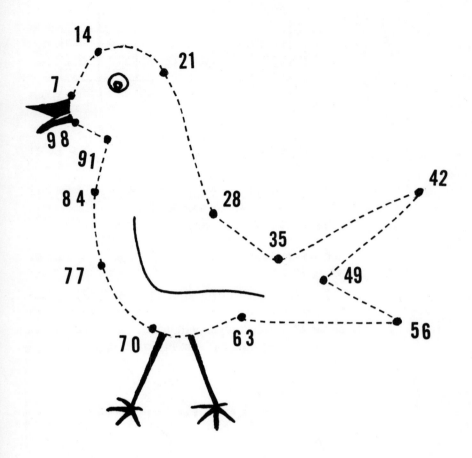

Seven Sequence   [2–4]

This game involves counting by sevens or other groups for the purpose of understanding numbers and the number family system.

Draw a simple picture on the board and then, in sequence, number points around the outline so that when the picture is erased, pupils may take turns connecting the numbers to recreate the original drawing.

In this illustration, have the child start at 7 and count by 7's in connecting the dots.

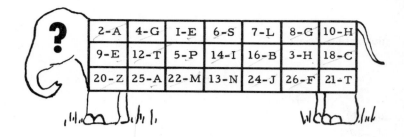

2-A	4-G	I-E	6-S	7-L	8-G	10-H
9-E	12-T	5-P	14-I	16-B	3-H	18-C
20-Z	25-A	22-M	13-N	24-J	26-F	21-T

A Secret Message   [2–4]

Cross out all the even numbered letters to find the name of this jungle animal. The remaining letters will spell the name of the animal in the picture.

In Round Figures   [2–4]

Place the figures 1 through 14 in the spots marked by the x's in the figure below so that each small circle of three figures will total 21. Some of the numbers have already been inserted, as you can see.

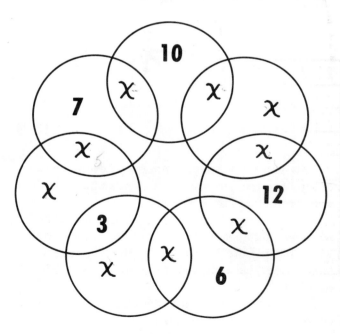

60   ■   *LEARNING DEVICES*

Construct this illustration board out of Masonite or heavy cardboard. Use 81 squares, with 9 across and 9 down. Push thumbtacks through the backs of all squares so that the points stick through the center of the empty squares. These points are to hold the little numbered squares in place when the game is being played.

Cut square pieces to fit the illustration board squares. Write a product of the multiplication facts on these little squares.

To play the game, the little squares are placed blank side up before the child (or children). A square is then picked up, turned over, and placed on the proper product square on the large board. Two boards and sets of numbers can be used for having a race. The child filling the board accurately first is the winner.

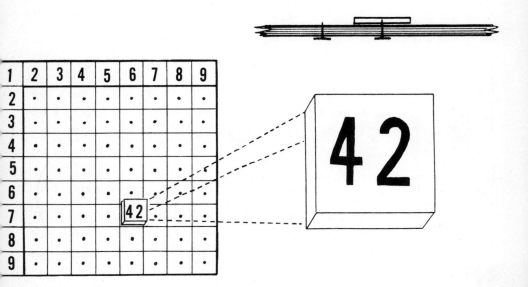

Row 1.

35	16	11	38	46	63	26	11	59
−23	+ 2	+10	−13	−28	−24	+17	+ 8	−42
12	18	(21)	(25)	18	(39)	(43)	19	17

Row 2.

28	57	35	55	70	18	33	27	17
− 9	−17	−18	−16	−28	+15	−19	+18	+18
19	(40)	17	39	(42)	33	14	(45)	35

Row 3.

91	44	64	73	87	92	48	91	46
−28	−18	−39	−41	−38	−36	−24	−39	−19
63	26	(25)	32	49	56	(24)	52	27

Row 4.

16	17	35	71	97	17	62	14	95
+ 8	+ 9	−17	−42	−81	+19	−34	+13	−82
24	26	18	(29)	16	(36)	28	27	13

Row 5.

48	51	87	72	62	25	70	90	21
+18	+19	−26	−19	−19	+22	+13	−46	+29
66	70	61	53	(43)	47	83	44	50

Although this example is done for you, have the pupils follow these directions:

1. Find the answers to all of the examples on the opposite page.

2. Put a ring around the *four largest answers* in Row 1.
   Put a ring around the *three largest answers* in Row 2.
   Put a ring around the *two smallest answers* in Row 3.
   Put a ring around the *two largest answers* in Row 4.
   Put a ring around the *smallest answer* in Row 5.

3. Starting in Row 1, with the largest answer, take a red crayon and going in a clockwise direction, draw a line to each of your circled answers.

   What is the picture?

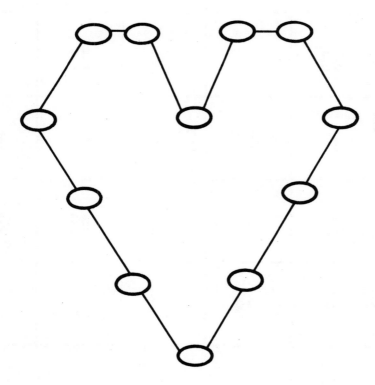

Children construct Matho boards from six-inch pieces of cardboard, ruling them so that there are 30 squares on each board. Place the letters: M-A-T-H-O in the top five squares. Under each of these letters write the products of multiplica-

M	A	T	H	O
27	32	24	48	20
63	35	28	36	18
56	42	**FREE**	81	16
72	40	25	45	35
96	28	14	12	21

tion combinations. These figures vary, as in Bingo. Each child has a set of small squares or paper (of any color) as markers.

One child acts as caller and calls out a multiplication fact under each of the five letters. A child having a card with the product of the fact covers that product on his card. The first child covering five squares in a straight or diagonal line wins the game and becomes the next caller.

Children should call back the number fact $(3 \times 9 = 27)$ as verification of the product that was covered on the card.

Wheel Multiplication [2–4]

Multiply the number on each spoke of the wheel by the middle number. Write the answer in the space outside the wheel.

The Leaf Game [2–4]

Around each leaf on page 66 write all the facts whose answers are the same as the answers in the leaf.

Making a Slide Rule [2–4]

Make a slide rule to be used in working out addition and subtraction problems or exercises. Use a piece of strong tagboard, $4\frac{1}{2}'' \times 20''$. Fold in half lengthwise to make the body of the slide rule. With

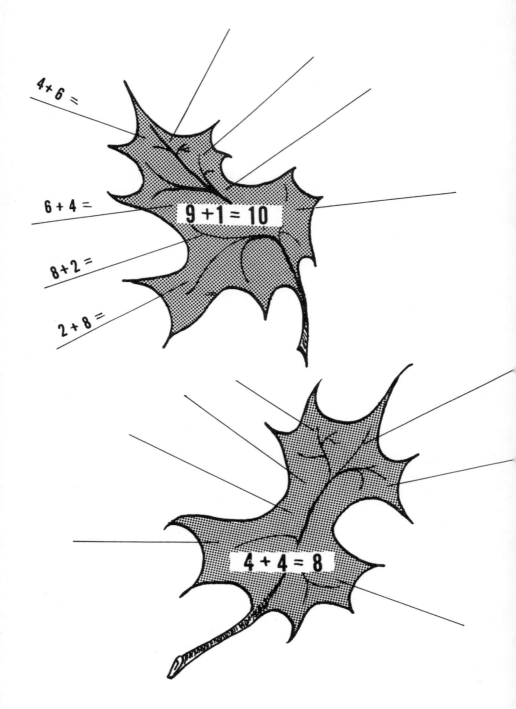

4 + 6 =

6 + 4 =

8 + 2 =

2 + 8 =

9 + 1 = 10

4 + 4 = 8

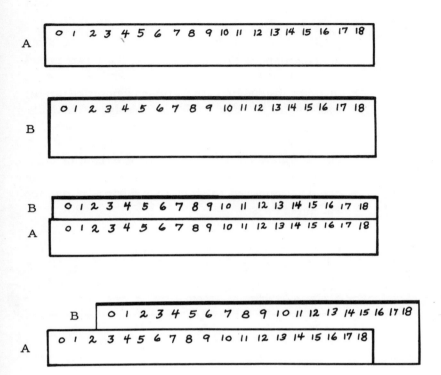

a Magic Marker or felt pen, write the numerals 0 through 18 at intervals of one inch, allowing one-eighth inch from the top. (See Drawing A.)

Use another piece of tagboard 3½″ × 20″ and write the numerals 0 through 18, two and one-half inches from the bottom of the tagboard. This is the *slide*. (See Drawing B.)

Place the slide in the body. Move the slide to the right until the zero is above one addend. Look along the slide for the second addend. In the illustration below, the second addend is the sum.

Illustration shown: $3 + 4 = 7$
or
$3 + 5 = 8$

Glue 20 empty thread spools (of the same size) along a narrow piece of wood at least two inches wide. Dowels or lollipop sticks, with appropriate pictures fastened to each, may be inserted in the spool holes to show addition or subtraction facts. Cardboard strips may be used to mark off facts.

The diagram below shows the concept $8 + 5$ which equals 13. Use the strips of oaktag or cardboard for separation purposes. The first separator could be removed to show that thirteen is one ten and three ones.

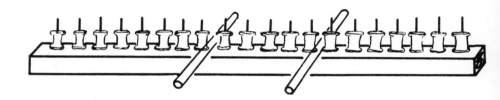

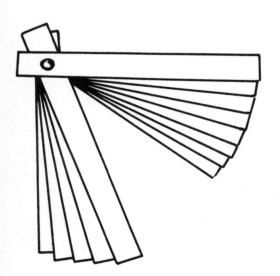

Cardboard Strip Reckoner [K–2]

Cut $1'' \times 4''$ cardboard strips with a punched hole in one corner of each strip. Use a roundhead fastener to hold the strips together. The number of strips used depends upon the sums and the minuends that are being subtracted or added by the children. The drawing at the left illustrates $13 - 8 = 5$.

How Many Squares?   [2–6]

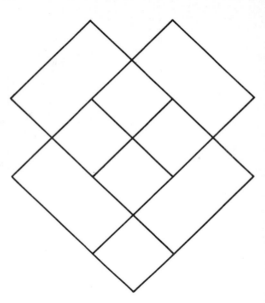

This is another exercise in counting and is also a new approach to the basic number skills.

There are many squares in this figure. The teacher asks how many of the children can count the squares, reminding them that the four sides of a square must be equal in length.

Answer: There are 11 squares.

Learning Odd Numbers   [2–3]

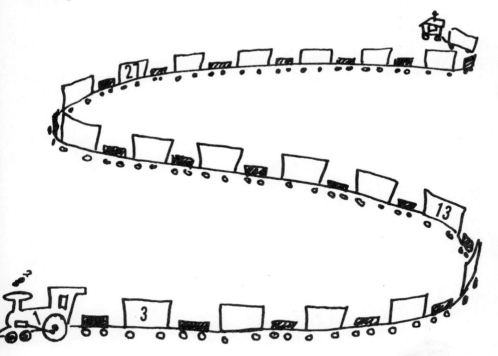

1	2		4		6		8		10
	12		14		16		18		20
	22		24		26		28		30
	32		34		36		38		40

Count the cars on this train and write in the numbers on the white cars. These numbers, starting with 1 and 3, are called odd numbers. Then fill in the missing odd numbers on the chart above.

Missing Fact Cards [2-4]

$$3 \times ? = 15$$

Cut some 6″ × 9″ cards from light colored paper or oaktag. Write facts with one number missing. In place of the missing number, staple a colored square, circle, or figure. Display around the room for mental arithmetic drill.

Circle of Facts [2-5]

Cut out two circles, about six inches in diameter, connected by a strip of heavy paper. Make a fold in the center of the strip so that the circles are superimposed and the strip can serve as a handle. Cut an arc out of the top circle on the outer edge, opposite the strip. Near the strip, cut a window, leaving on the flap. Cut circles and insert, with the combinations showing through the arc and the answers under the flaps. Fasten in the center with a round head paper fastener, so that the inserted circle will turn.

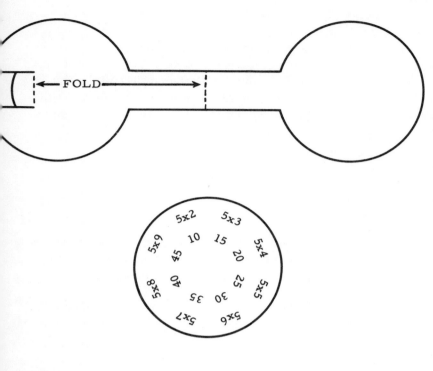

Lotto

On separate slips of paper, write numbers from 1 to 20. On a small piece of writing paper, the players prepare cards bearing one-half-inch squares. They fill in problems in all the arithmetical processes, depending on the grade for which this is being used. Each player makes up his own problems. The problems must be such that the answers range from 1 to 20. The slips bearing 1 to 20 are deposited in a hat.

5 +4	6 +7	9 +1 10
9 +4	7 +2	10 +2

10

The teacher draws a number and calls out the number aloud. If the answer to one of their problems is called, the players write the answer in the square below the problem. Of course, not all players write every time a number is called. The first player to fill a specified number of squares raises his hand and calls "Lotto." He is the winner.

Card Matching [2–4]

This game calls for matching numbers written with figures and with words. It is designed to develop facility in the number system, especially at the lower grades.

Construct a set of cards showing numbers in figures, and a corresponding set with the same number given in words.

| **6 0 9** | **six hundred nine** |

| **1 9 5 8** | **nineteen fifty-eight** |

Place the cards with the figures along the chalk tray, and the others in a box. Divide the class into teams and alternately allow a member from each team to pick a card from the box. He must try to match the card with its equivalent on the chalk tray. Doing so, he keeps both cards. The team that retains the most cards is the winner.

The Double Chart

[2-4]

This activity involves showing three-place numbers in two ways: either in a pocket chart, or on the chalkboard. It further emphasizes familiarity with numbers along with place value.

A three-place number is written. A member from each team must show the number written as hundreds, tens and ones in another pocket chart or chalkboard. The chart can be utilized for a host of arithmetical concepts.

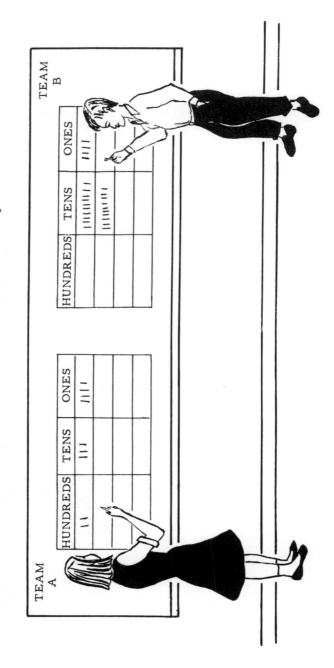

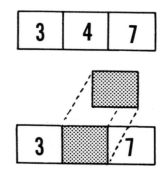

Number Combination Cards [2–4]

To strengthen relationships of number combinations, use these number combination cards.

Place a number combination, in three blocks, on strips of paper 4″ × 6″, and fold back 1″ toward the center at the short edge. Slide a flash card over the strip so that it covers one number. The children are to supply the missing number.

Single Line Abacus [K–2]

Obtain a small box that is open at the top. Punch holes in each end of the box near the top and use a

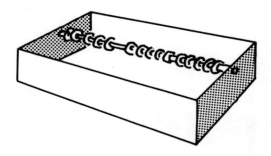

double string with ten buttons on the string. Use this device as a counting frame for numbers 1 to 10.

Materials for Teaching Fractions [2–4]

Paper plates can be cut into halves, or they may be marked into sections and labeled. If whole plates are used, construct an extra set so that children may play with them as a jig-saw puzzle. However, do not restrict the teaching of fractional parts to spherical objects. Use rectangles, a long piece of string, and other dimensions in order for children to understand fractional partition.

Squares and other geometric shapes may be cut from felt and used on a flannel board. Recognition of the concept of one-half is illustrated on page 75.

Are the light and dark parts the same size?

The Beanbag Game [2–4]

Draw a diagram, similar to the one below, on the floor. Several feet away, draw a line, behind which the pupils stand and throw a beanbag at the center square marked nine. Each pupil is given two throws, and his score is the sum of the two numbers he hits. In order to earn this score, the pupil must state the sum correctly. Either individual or team scores can be kept.

The game can be varied in such ways that it gives different types of drills. It can also be used to develop the meaning of zero and facts involving zero, by requiring the individual to record a zero score when he misses the target entirely or by marking one of the squares with a zero. This can be used for all the arithmetical processes.

1	8	4
5	9	0
3	7	2

Playing Fireman   [2–3]

A picture is drawn on the board showing a house with smoke coming out of the roof. The front is cut away to show various items of furniture, on each of which is written an arithmetical combination. The pupils play fireman and rescue the furniture from the burning house by stating the combinations correctly. Rescue by erasing it. The fun is rescuing the big pieces which have been labeled with more difficult facts.

The ladder game may also be employed here. Place a ladder at the window. Each rung of the ladder has a number combination. This variation gives the children added incentive.

A Magic Rectangle   [2–4]

8	15	1
2		13
11	3	
14		4
5		

Add the numbers in the first horizontal row. Supply each of the missing numbers in the other rows so that each row will have an equal sum.

Add the numbers in the vertical row. Add the numbers so that each row down will also have sums that are equal.

A Magic Circle   [2–4]

Add the numbers around each of the three circles.

Then add the numbers on each of the straight lines.

Your answers should always be the same.

This activity promotes the understanding of measures by providing practice in giving equivalents for measuring units.

Make a set of cards containing the information shown below on both the front and back of the cards.

Place the cards face up on a table and let pairs of pupils take turns trying to supply the missing number. If this is done correctly, the pupil wins the card; otherwise, he places it in a separate pile for later study. The pupil with the most cards at the end of the game wins.

3 ft. = ? in.	**(36)**
front	back

1yd. = ? ft.	**(3)**
front	back

144 sq. in. = ? sq. ft.

FRONT

(1)

BACK

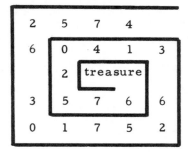

$$
\begin{array}{cccccc}
2 & 3 & 7 & 2 & 6 & 6 \\
+\,3 & \times\,3 & -\,1 & \times\,3 & -\,3 & \times\,2 \\[4pt]
1 & 3 & 3 & 6 & 6 & 3 \\
\times\,5 & -\,2 & +\,5 & -\,5 & +\,1 & -\,2 \\[4pt]
2 & 4 & 7 & 7 & 6 & 3 \\
+\,2 & +\,1 & -\,2 & -\,5 & -\,1 & \times\,3 \\[4pt]
2 & 7 & 7 & 7 & 6 & 6 \\
+\,2 & -\,6 & +\,4 & \times\,4 & +\,5 & -\,2 \\[4pt]
5 & 6 & 2 & 2 & 2 & 4 \\
-\,4 & -\,1 & \times\,4 & +\,5 & -\,1 & +\,3 \\[4pt]
3 & 4 & 3 & 3 & 5 & 2 \\
+\,4 & -\,1 & \times\,3 & -\,1 & +\,3 & \times\,5 \\
\end{array}
$$

Directional Puzzle [3–4]

Can you find your way out of this puzzle?
Solve the examples and find your way out.

A Treasure Hunt [3–4]

```
2   5   7   4
6   0   4   1   3
    2  treasure
3   5   7   6   6
0   1   7   5   2
```

1. Multiply each number shown on the trail by 5.

2. Multiply each number by 5 again, but now add 4 to each product.

To construct this practical, adjustable thermometer, use a 36″ by 8″ piece of oaktag or plywood. About five inches from each end make a cut about two inches long (slits A

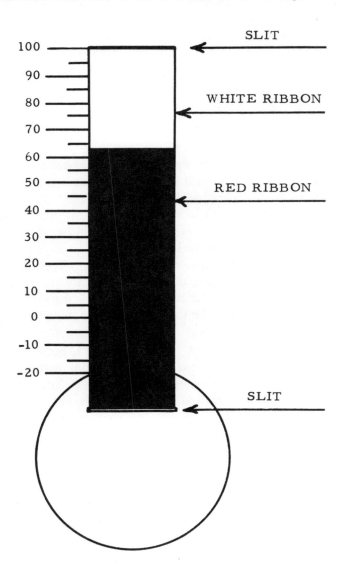

and B). Get a piece of red and white ribbon, each one-half inch longer than the distance between the slits. Sew the ribbons end to end. Insert one end through one slit, and the other end through the opposite slit. Sew the free ends together to make one continuous, movable strip of ribbon. Two inch ribbon is recommended for the width.

Mark the Fahrenheit scale along the oaktag or plywood between the two slits. Paint a red bulb around point B to resemble the base of the thermometer. Have the child adjust the thermometer daily, according to the one found in your classroom.

Flexible Hundred Board [3–4]

Obtain a piece of ½-inch plywood that is about 30 inches square. Mark off the board into 100 squares—10 rows of 10 squares each, making each square about 2½ inches on a side. Center and screw a small L-hook near the top of each square so that the round, metal key tags will be within the squares when hung from the L-hooks.

Secure about 200 round, metal-rimmed key tags, 100 of one color and another 100 of a different color. On each set of 100 key tags write the numerals from 1 through 100. The sets of key tags may be used on the board in many ways.

1. Hang one set of key tags on the L-hooks to make the hundred board. In dealing with the serial order of numbers, one or more key tags may be removed or turned with the blank side out to show the missing numeral in a series.

2. The Hundred Board may be used in work with the tens and ones structure of numbers. To show a number such as 37, hang 37 key tags in 3 rows of 10, and 7 key tags in the fourth row.

HUNDRED BOARD

Crossword Puzzles [3–6]

Fill in the empty squares with the sign that shows what arithmetic process was used to get the numbers in the bottom row, and also in the far right row of squares.

The top row in Box I is done for you.

I

1	×	6	÷	2	≈	3
9		2		8	=	3
5		3		2		6
≈		≈		≈		≈
5		6		8	=	3

II

9		3		7	=	10
6		2		8	=	4
4		5		5	=	4
=		=		=		=
7		1		10	=	18

III

2		8		4	=	4
6		8		3		16
4		1		7	=	11
≈		≈		≈		≈
3		1		5	=	9

IV

4		3		6	=	6
8		2		1	=	3
3		4		2	=	0
≈		≈		≈		
9		1		5	=	13

V

6		2		3		9
4		1		2		2
6		1		2		3
=		≈		≈		≈
18		1		8	=	10

VI

3		4		6	=	2
2		3		4	=	10
7		6		2	=	11
=		≈		=		≈
13		6		4	=	23

This is an effective game for problem solving. It combines game motivation and writing on the chalkboard.

Make a large spinner on oaktag, with sections numbered 1 to 10, and pin it on the bulletin board. Then, on the chalkboard, write and number 10 different numerical problems. Pupils from alternate teams take turns spinning the wheel to discover which of the numbered problems must be attempted. If the problem is solved correctly, the team initial should be written in front of it. The object is for the team to be first to solve all problems correctly. If the spinner lands on a number for a problem that has already been solved, the next pupil immediately takes his turn at the spinner.

This game is designed for pairs of pupils, or small groups of children. In this case, the problems may be placed on numbered cards, with the answers on the reverse side for verification. The game may be further varied by having pupils work, in turn, each of the numbered problems. After each correct answer, the player spins the wheel to discover how many points he will receive for his answer. The team or pupil with the most points at the end of the game is the winner.

Discovering Numbers [2–6]

Fill in the blank columns in each of the puzzles below. The first column in each box is done for you.

				Write a number.
8				Multiply it by 2.
16				Add 6 to it.
22				Divide by 2.
11				Subtract the first number.
3				What answer do you get every time?

				Write a number.
4				Multiply it by 2.
8				Add 10.
18				Divide by 2.
9				Subtract the first number.
5				What answer do you get every time?

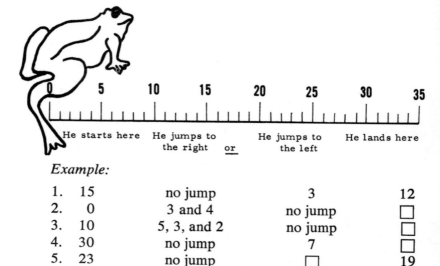

He starts here   He jumps to   He jumps to   He lands here
the right   or   the left

Example:

		He jumps to the right	or	He jumps to the left	He lands here
1.	15	no jump		3	12
2.	0	3 and 4		no jump	☐
3.	10	5, 3, and 2		no jump	☐
4.	30	no jump		7	☐
5.	23	no jump		☐	19
6.	10	☐ ☐		no jump	19
7.	☐	5		no jump	13
8.	☐	no jump		4	17
9.	29	no jump		7	☐

Answers: 1–12, 2–7, 3–20, 4–23, 5–4, 6–5, 4, 7–8,
8–21, 9–22

Learning Terms [4–6]

Prepare several cards in such a way that each contains an example with one factor outlined to illustrate an arithmetic term. On the back of each write the correct answer. The card for the word "minuend" might appear as below.

$$24$$
$$-$$
$$18$$

REMAINDER

MINUEND

$$8$$
$$-$$
$$7$$

86 ▪

Place the cards in the middle of a table and let a group of pupils take turns selecting and displaying the cards one by one. Every pupil writes on a sheet of lined paper the term he thinks is called for by each card. The card is then turned over and each pupil corrects his own answer by placing a check mark or an X beside it. The one with the most check marks wins. Pupils who miss several words should study them and play the game again.

Abbreviations [4–6]

Write several measurement units on the board and have pupils try to write the correct abbreviations for each. This may be played as a relay race in which two lists are used and teams compete in trying to write all the abbreviations first. It may also be given as an assignment to small groups of pupils.

Numberland Game [4–6]

This activity is designed to strengthen the meanings of numbers. It consists of a large oaktag playing board and a spinner with numbers 1–4 written on it. Numbered cards may be used instead of a spinner.

Pupils take turns spinning or drawing cards. This tells them how many spaces to advance. If the correct answer is not given, the child loses his turn. When a child lands on a square where directions are given, he must follow them without any help.

It is wise to have a duplicate of the playing board on a separate piece of paper so that disputed answers may be clarified. Any pupil who challenges a correct answer may lose a turn or go back a space.

The first child finished is the winner.

NUMBERLAND GAME

START	470 = ? tens	248 = ? hundreds and ? tens and ? ones	Forgot something? Go back to start.	100 tens = ?
Red Light Lose 1 turn	803 = ? tens and ? ones	13 hundreds and 4 ones = ?	Down Hill. Go forward 1	short cut. Advance 4 spaces
307 = 3 hundreds and ? tens and ? ones	NUMBERLAND GAME	No gas. Go back 3 places.	10 x 56 = ? tens	8 tens and 14 ones = ?
Up Hill Go back 1.	900, 090 = ? thousands and ? ones	60 hundreds = ?	Super Highway 1 extra turn	5,490 = ? hundreds and ? tens and ones?

How many pairs equal 89?

1	2	3	4	5	6	7	8	9	10
1	12	13	14	15	16	17	18	19	20
1	22	23	24	25	26	27	28	29	30
1	32	33	34	35	36	37	38	39	40
1	42	43	44	45	46	47	48	49	50
1	52	53	54	55	56	57	58	59	60
1	62	63	64	65	66	67	68	69	70
1	72	73	74	75	76	77	78	79	80
1	82	83	84	85	86	87	88	89	90
1	92	93	94	95	96	97	98	99	100

There are 36 pairs of numbers on this chart
which equal 89 when added together. If you
know how, you can find them easily.

Hint: Add the numbers in opposite corners
in each square.

Football Game   **[4–6]**

Draw a football field on the board, or on oaktag if it is to
be reused. Show the yardage lines, as in the illustration
on page 90.

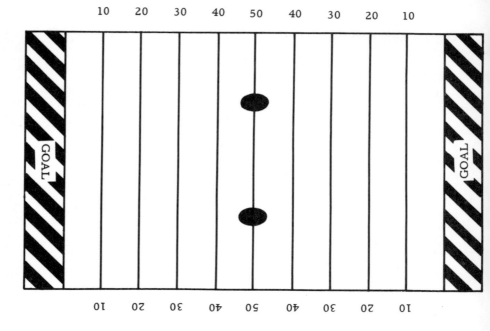

Make a set of cards with fraction examples on one side and answers on the other. Shuffle the cards and place them with the example side up in the middle of a table. The players draw cards in turn and give answers for the examples. The game starts at the 50 yard line and players move their markers towards opposite goals. For correct answers, players move 10 yards forward; for incorrect answers, 10 yards backwards. Six points are received for crossing the goal line and one extra point is given if the next card is correctly answered. The marker is then returned to the 50 yard line and the game is continued. When the cards are exhausted, the player or team with the most points wins.

Map Treasure Hunt [4–6]

Duplicate the directions and the map shown opposite for each pupil in your class. At the signal to

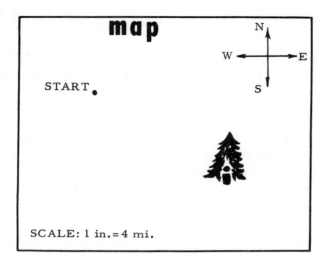

SCALE: 1 in.=4 mi.

start, the pupils use their rulers and the scale to mark off on the map the route given by the directions. They should mark with a small x the spot where they think the treasure is buried. All pupils who place their x near a point ⅝ inches south and ¾ inches east of the starting point may be declared the winner.

Directions:

Use the scale and make a dot,
Seven miles east of the starting spot.
Then set out for the base of the tree
And measure off a mile very carefully.

Now go south for a little while,
To be exact—for a half a mile.
Turn and travel nine miles west
But don't stop to take a rest.

Face to the right (you'll be heading north)
And travel straight for a mile and a fourth.
Aim for the tree—at the dot in the middle—
And go five miles to complete the riddle.

   Show the flight of a rocket with division marks in which are written examples involving decimals, as shown below. Then, make out a set of small cards containing several duplicates of each of the examples written in the rocket's flight. Write the correct answer on the back of each card. Each of three or four pupils is provided with a marker (perhaps a small cutout of a rocket) which is placed on the "Earth" at the start of the game.

   Pupils play by shuffling and passing out the cards, placing them with the example-side up in front of them, and reading each card in turn. If a pupil reads a card that matches the one in the space in front of his marker, he may advance if he can give a reasonable estimate for the example. The first to reach the satellite wins.

The teacher says, "I'm thinking of something in this room that is about 60 inches long," and then calls on volunteers to guess what it is. When a pupil guesses correctly, he becomes the leader and continues the procedure.

It would be wise for each pupil-leader to check with the teacher regarding the estimate of length he is going to give so that the rest of the class will be given a fairly accurate estimate on which to base their guessing.

Answer: Start out with a pupil about five feet tall.

Upside-down Magic Square   [4–6]

The two diagonals and every row and column in this square add up to 264. Now look at the second figure in which letters are used to indicate the squares in the magic square diagram.

A, B, C, and D add up to 264. So do E, F, G, and H, and I, J, K, and L. Turn the square upside down and the numbers will still add up to 264.

There are about 48 ways of making 264 from this magic square. How many can you find?

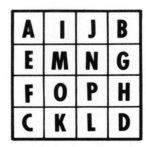

Answer: Have the pupils add up the letters indicated above first. Then have them
choose other number combinations
in order to find the correct total.

Raceway Game   **[4–6]**

Prepare a playingboard and a spinner similar to the one
shown below. For the playingboard shown, four players (or
four teams) may compete, and each should be provided
with a marker, such as a cut-out of a horse.

At the start all markers should be placed at the starting
line, and players should take turns twirling the spinner to
determine how far to advance the horses each time. This
continues until one marker finishes and is declared the
winner. Each pupil should keep a score sheet. These should
be checked at the end of the game for correctness.

To adapt the game to the review of subtraction, markers
may be placed at the finish line and moved backward as
numbers selected by the spinner are subtracted each time.

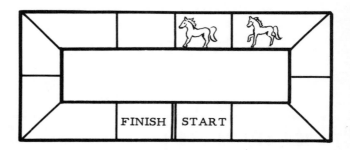

Decimal Relay   **[4–6]**

Write two sets of fractions in columns on the board in
such a way that both sets have the same fractions, but in a
different order. Divide the class into teams and explain that

when you give the signal to start, the first member on each team must go to the board and write the decimal equivalent beside the first fraction in his team's column.

As soon as the member returns to his seat, the next member writes a decimal equivalent for the next fraction, and so on until the list is completed. The team which writes the most correct decimal equivalents wins.

Lattice Multiplication [4–6]

Look at the following examples. Place the products within the proper bisected rectangles. Add diagonally for the sum!

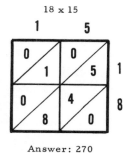

Answer: 270

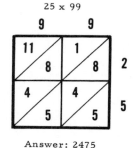

Answer: 2475

Problem Lattice Multiplication [4–6]

The diameter of the earth is estimated at 7900 miles. Find the circumference of the earth by the lattice multiplication. Use Pi = 3.14 × 7900.

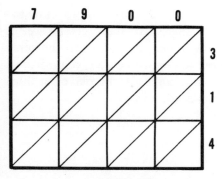

Answer: 24,806 Miles

■ 95

Another method of review of the basic number facts and the four processes is this game which involves giving answers for number facts.

Draw a baseball diamond on the board and place a number in the pitcher's box, as shown below.

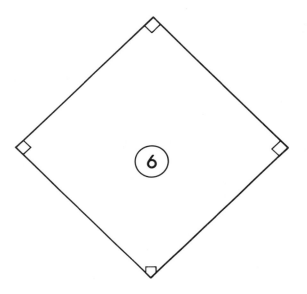

A player from one of two teams decides whether he will try for a single, double, triple, or home run. If he tries for a triple, the teacher gives him a hard addition, subtraction, multiplication, or division fact using the number in the pitcher's box. If he gives a correct answer, place an X at third base to show the presence of a player there. An incorrect answer is scored as an out. If the next player, from the same team, tries for a double (he would be given a fact of medium difficulty) and makes it, the player at third base is advanced home, for a score.

After three outs the other team takes over for the last half of the first inning. The number in the pitcher's box should be changed after each inning. The team with the highest score after nine innings wins.

The Magic Star [5–6]

1. Add the four fractions on each straight line of the star. There are six lines with fractions on them.

2. Add the fractions at the corners of each of the two triangles that form the star. First, add the fractions in the circles with the lines, such as $^{11}/_{16} + ^{3}/_{4} + ^{7}/_{16}$. Now add the fractions in the plain circles: $^{1}/_{2}$, $^{13}/_{16}$, $^{9}/_{16}$. Are the answers the same?

3. Next, add the fractions at the corners of small triangle A: $^{1}/_{2}$, $^{5}/_{16}$, $^{1}/_{4}$. Then add the fractions at the corners of each of the triangles marked B, C, D, E, and F. Are the answers the same?

Answers:

1. $1^{11}/_{16}$

2. Yes. . . . $1^{7}/_{8}$

3. Yes. . . . $1^{1}/_{16}$

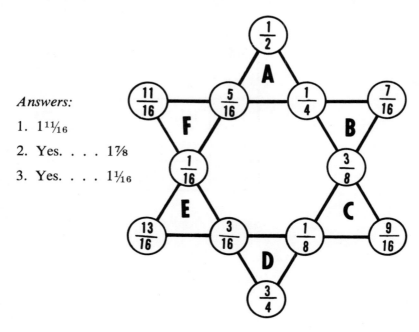

Problem: Ask someone to select a number from each column in the square drawn below. You can find the answer before he begins to add the numbers together on paper.

Solution: Add the last digit of each number selected. Subtract this result from 50. Your first answer will give you the *last* two digits of the number you are looking for, and the second answer (the difference) will give you the first two digits.

Example:

Add 366	Add last digits
543	6
582	3
954	2
872	4
	2
	17

69	345	186	872	756
366	642	582	278	558
168	246	87	575	657
762	147	285	377	954
663	543	483	179	855
564	48	384	674	459

Subtract from 50

$$50 - 17 = 33$$

Answer: 3317

This is a device which you can use hundreds of times in all subject matter areas. They can be purchased, or better still, make one yourself.

Obtain a piece of plywood 20″ x 28″. Stretch the flannel of a good background color (red, black, green) over the plywood board. Glue and tack loose ends on the back of the board.

Use felt figures for demonstration lessons. Figures cut from construction paper must have a backing of a sandpaper strip or scraps of felt in order to adhere to the board. Simple geometric figures are useful, as well as pictures of objects familiar to children.

Place Value Chart   **[K–6]**

Every teacher is familiar with the place value chart or pocket chart, but many times she is confused as to how

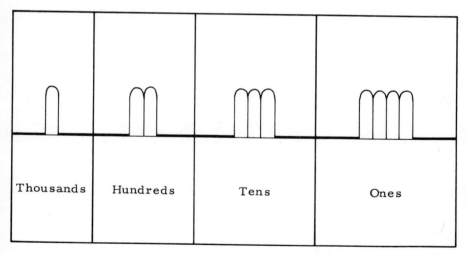

Example shown: 1, 234

to construct one. Since this chart plays an important part in the curriculum, directions for its construction are included here.

A durable place value chart can be made out of heavy tagboard or oak tag. Use a size about 18" x 22". Along the bottom of the tagboard place a strip of oaktag, about 2½ inches wide, and staple as shown in the diagram. Letter the pockets as shown.

Make from oaktag one hundred 5" x 1" strips to be used as counters. Bundle them in groups of ten, using rubber bands. If desired, colored tongue depressers may be used.

GAMES

All children like games! Games that are designed as a supplemental enrichment activity for learning specific numerical or operational concepts in arithmetic can also be fun. Teachers must be discreet in their application, and should always remember that games are not a substitute for an operational process, but rather a reinforcement or enrichment process for that particular arithmetical exercise.

Games can be used as a "before school" exercise activity, or they can be used to precede the formal lesson itself. Actually, the role of the game is dependent upon the concept that is being taught, and there is no specific rule of time when a game should be applied. Much depends upon the interest of the group, the ability of the pupils to understand and apply the arithmetical concept being taught, and the availability of materials required by the game itself.

It is important to remember, however, that games should involve as many students as possible. Therefore, it is necessary to provide an abundance of games, some involving as little as two or three pupils, and others involving as many as ten or fifteen pupils. Games should be kept in

■ 103

GAMES

marked containers, such as empty cartons or plastic boxes, and should be located on a shelf in the classroom and accessible to all youngsters at game time, or when they have finished their regular classwork.

Children should be encouraged to think of new games and they should be allowed to contribute materials for games that are used by the group. Also, as an exercise in locating information, children should be referred to the many practical sources for discovering "new games," such as the information found in magazines, newspapers, journals, and various types of books.

Games should be used as frequently as the children enjoy them. If you see the class becoming listless or apathetic toward formal arithmetic teaching, then introduce a game. Be sure to keep a file handy of all the games that are available and that you plan to use in your teaching. List them under special topics such as multiplication, fractions, measurement, and so forth.

The children's enthusiasm and the practicality of the game itself will determine how successful you have been in its application in the classroom.

Arranging or Ordering Numbers [K–2]

Numerals are cut from the pages of old calendars and pasted on cardboard. (Paste the entire page on a sheet of cardboard and cut individual number squares with a paper cutter.) Pupils lay the numbers on their tables (or desks) in proper sequence, as far as they can count.

Bouncing the Ball [K–2]

The pupils count silently as the teacher bounces a rubber ball. A pupil is called upon to state the last number counted (as the teacher momentarily halts the bouncing). If correct, the child bounces the ball the remaining number of times needed to reach a prestated number. He then starts a new series of bounces and calls upon another pupil.

Buzz-Buzz [K–2]

The members of the class count by turns. A certain number is agreed upon. When that number is reached in the counting, the child counting says "Buzz" instead of the number. If he misses, by saying the number, he must say "Buzz" the number of times there are numbers between the one he missed and the highest number he can count.

Fox and Chickens [K–2]

Counting blocks (1" × 1") representing chickens are laid on pupils' desks or tables. Several pupils close their eyes as the "foxes" take chickens from them. At a signal, they open their eyes and report how many chickens are missing.

I Can Match That Number [K–2]

Make three cards for each number through 10. For example, write 2, two, and II (Roman numeral). Each pupil takes a card. In turn, pupils go to the front of the room and show cards to the class. Other pupils having cards containing the same number written in a different way stand beside the first child and display their cards.

I Have That Number [K–2]

Make a set of cards on which are written the numbers from one through one hundred. The cards are distributed to the class. The teacher begins counting aloud, slowly. The pupils bring up their cards as their numbers are called. If someone misses his number, it is repeated once. Those who hold cards after the number one hundred is called go to the front of the room and state the number that precedes the one they hold.

Matching Cards

Make four-card sets for each of the numbers from one through five. In each set, one card should show the name, as "two." Another should show the numeral, as "2." A third should have two dots, or lines, as: :, . . , or //. The fourth card should have small pictures of two objects, as a pair of birds. The cards are shuffled and distributed. In turn, the pupils stand before the class and show the card held. All the pupils who hold the same number in another form rise and stand beside the first child, showing their cards.

Lotto [K–2]

The lotto cards are made by ruling off twenty 1-inch squares on 4″ × 5″ rectangles of paper (pupils may do this, or they may be mimeographed). The numbers from 1 through 20 are written in the squares in random order. The numbers from 1 through 20 are also written on 20 small cards suitable for drawing out of a box. Each pupil has a master sheet consisting of the 20 squares, and is issued 5 cardboard markers. The 20 small cards are shuffled in a box, and drawn out one at a time. As the teacher draws and announces a number, each player covers the number on his card with a marker. The first player to cover five numbers in a row raises his hand and calls "Lotto," winning the game.

Number Guessing Game [K–2]

The teacher places a row of number cards in a card

holder. A pupil is selected to hide his eyes while a number is taken from the holder. He then guesses the missing number.

Postman [K–2]

Use two sets of number cards. One player is chosen to be the postman and is given one set of number cards. The other set of cards is placed on "houses" (the desks) of other players. The postman must match his cards with those on the "houses." When he misses, the person who lives in the house becomes the next postman.

Tens and Ones [K–2]

Choose one child to stand before the group and make a statement such as this: "I am thinking of a number that is one ten and three ones. Those who think they know what the number is, raise your hands." The leader calls on someone to go to the board to write the number, which in this case is 13. If what the latter writes is correct, he becomes leader.

Arabic Number [K–2]

Choose one child to be IT. IT selects and calls any number that has been studied by all members of the group, perhaps a number between 1 and 100. Any member of the group may be called on to arrange the beads on the abacus to show the number called. If he is correct, he becomes IT.

(This game can also be played by using the counting box, sometimes called the "place-value box.")

Scramble [K–2]

Select two teams of ten players each. Give each team a set of number cards to be distributed among the members. The teacher or an umpire calls a number from 10 to 99. If the number called is 37, the players who have the numbers 3 and 7 must arrange themselves to face the teacher and the other players, holding their cards so that the correct number is shown. The team whose members make the correct numbers first scores a point. No assistance may be given by team members whose numbers are not involved. Other numbers are called, and the game proceeds until time is called.

Number Party [K–2]

Several children sit in a corner. A group of other children are given numbers. One of the children in the second group comes to the first group and says, "May I come to your party?" and taps his number on the floor or wall. The children in the corner say, "Yes, Five (or whatever the number is), you may come in." Other guests approach in the same way. The children in the corner may take turns inviting the other children to the party.

Basketball [K–2]

Place a wastebasket or box in an open space. Draw a line six to eight feet away from the container.

Have players stand behind the line and take turns throwing bean bags into the basket. Each child gets five to ten throws. He then counts the number of bean bags in the basket to figure his score.

Pegs [K–2]

Each child is given several cards and a handful of markers. The children place the correct number of markers on each number card. For example, six markers should be placed on the card on which the number 6 appears, four markers on card number 4, and so on.

Ten Little Indians [K–2]

The pupil group sings the *Ten Little Indian* song as ten children, each holding a number card, step forward in numerical sequence according to the song. They step backward during the second verse as their turns come again.

The Train [K–2]

Several small chairs are placed in a row. These constitute the "train." Children, as passengers, take their seats in the chairs. One pupil, selected to be "conductor," stands beside the pupil in the first chair. A card showing a number is flashed. If the conductor names it first, he retains his job. If the passenger names it first, he becomes the conductor.

When the conductor loses his job, he takes the last seat and all passengers move up.

As I Remember [K–2]

Pupils are selected by lot (or volunteer) to go to the chalkboard and write from memory all combinations that add to 12, 13, 14, etc., or the subtraction combinations with a given remainder.

Baseball [K–2]

Organize the class into teams. Designate home plate, and the three bases at appropriate places in the classroom. Teams select pitchers who "throw" problems at the batters in turn. Correct answers advance players one base. Four problems answered correctly and a player reaches "home" and scores a run. If he misses on any base he is "out" and another player goes to bat.

Bean Bag [K–2]

There are numerous variations of this game, adapted to the needs for practice on various topics. For practice on addition and subtraction combinations, this version is useful:

Each player throws two (or three, at a more advanced level) bean bags at a numbered target. His score is the total of the throws. If the bag falls on a line separating numbered zones, the score is the number from the zone in which the larger part of the bag lies. Practice in subtraction can be provided by subtracting the lower of the throws from the higher number hit by the bean bag.

Breaking Through the Lines [K–2]

A goal line is marked off, and "guards" appointed. Pupils take turns trying to reach the goal line by giving the combinations to addition or subtraction questions asked by the "guards." This game may also be used for multiplication and division.

I Bought [K–2]

This type of computation with whole numbers concerns the addition of columns of digits without paper and pencil. As such it serves as a mental exercise.

A pupil starts the game by saying something like, "I bought an ice cream cone for 5¢." The next pupil repeats this and continues, saying, "I bought an ice cream cone for 5¢ and a newspaper for 7¢. They cost 12¢." The next player says, "I bought an ice cream cone for 5¢, a newspaper for 7¢ and a lollipop for 4¢. They cost 16¢." This continues until a pupil gives an incorrect response, in which case he drops out, and the next player starts another series. Slower learners may be allowed to write the figures to be added on a sheet of paper.

Christmas Stocking [K–2]

Stocking-shaped pieces, approximately six inches

long, are cut from red paper, in pairs. (Double the paper and cut, to be sure of getting exact duplicates.) Number combinations are pasted on stockings in such an arrangement that each pair of stockings has two combinations with the same answer (as, "5 + 4" and "7 + 2"). Stockings are distributed about the room singly. Pupils are given one of a pair, find the other by matching combination answers, and pin them on a Christmas tree.

Climb the Ladder [K–2]

The teacher draws a "ladder" on the chalkboard with a combination for each rung. Pupils climb the ladder by giving the sums or remainders correctly. If a pupil makes a mistake, he falls one rung, two rungs, or more, depending on the difficulty of the combination (agreed upon in advance).

Combination Solitaire [K–2]

Make a chart containing approximately 9 to 15 rectangular spaces about 4″ by 6″ in size, each containing the answer to a combination. Small combination cards, about 3″ by 4″ in size, are made with the combination on one side, the answer on the other. The pupil playing the game selects a card, answers the combination, and then turns the card over to check his answer. If his answer was correct, he puts the card, answer-side up, in the proper space on the chart. If his answer was incorrect, he places the card on the chart with the combination-side up. At the end of the game, the number of right-side-up cards gives the score. The teacher can tell at a glance which combinations need to be studied.

Dog and His Bone [K–2]

The children draw numbers to see who is the "Dog." The chosen one sits in the center of the circle, blindfolded. Around him are scattered 8 to 12 cards containing number combinations. At a signal, some pupil in the circle attempts to reach the center of the circle and get a number card before the "Dog" discovers him. If the pupil gets a "bone" (number card) and gives the sum or difference for the combination, he scores. If he can't give the answer, the "Dog" is given a chance and, if he knows the answer, makes a score. If the blindfolded "Dog" detects a contestant trying to get a combination, he barks. If he makes a mistake in the location of the person trying to get a "bone," he loses and the other pupil scores. The game continues until the "Dog" has lost all of his bones. A new "Dog" is then selected.

Finding a Number [K–2]

One pupil, to be IT, is selected by lot and sits in the center of a circle formed by the other pupils. IT announces the number that is to be the sum; for example, "nine." He then announces one of the two numbers whose sum is nine, and calls on a pupil in the circle to name the other number. If the answer is correct, IT names another sum, gives one of its factors, and calls on the next pupil around the circle for the other factor. If the pupil called on misses, he becomes IT.

Fish Pond [K–2]

Similar to "Gathering Acorns." Cut out fish-shaped

pieces of tagboard, six to eight inches long. Write number combinations on them and scatter them in the "pond" (a basket, a corner of the floor, etc.). Giving the correct answer to a combination catches the fish.

Fox and Geese [K–2]

Numbers are drawn to select the "Fox," who is placed in the center of a circle. He calls on one of the "geese" composing the circle for the answer to a combination such as $4 + 3$ or $7 - 5$. If the person named cannot answer, the "goose" is caught and joins the "fox" in the center. The "fox" calls another combination. If the "goose" that is "caught" can answer before the "goose" in the circle, or if the pupil in the circle makes a mistake, and the "caught goose" (in the center) then answers, he escapes back into the circle.

Gathering Acorns [K–2]

"Acorns" are cut from tagboard, approximately four inches in diameter. Calendar numbers are pasted on the acorns, with space between for writing the addition or subtraction sign, as $7 - 4$, or $2 + 3$. The "acorns" are scattered about the room (in the bookshelves, on the chalk tray, on window ledges, and elsewhere). Children are chosen to be squirrels, and gather "acorns" only as they are able to give the correct sum or difference to the number on the "acorns" they find. "Let's see how many acorns we can store up for the winter!" is a good way to start.

Guess What It Is [K–2]

Make a number of 4″ by 6″ cards (or 6″ by 8″, if large stickers are used). On one side write number combinations, as $3 + 2 = 5$. On the other side paste stickers, five in a row for the card having the combination adding to 5. The child who is IT draws a card, notes the grouping of stickers, and says, "There are five spots on the card." He then turns the card over to see the combination, and the other pupils take turns guessing: "Is it $4 + 1$? Is it $3 + 2$? The child who guesses correctly then is IT.

Hide and Say [K–2]

Prepare for each pupil a coat hanger wire with 10 beads or oaktag squares strung on it. One pupil, selected as IT, turns his back and conceals some beads on each end of his wire by covering them with his folded hands. He then mentally subtracts the number of beads in his left hand from ten. Turning around, he announces the remainder. The correct answer is the number of beads concealed in the right hand. Children take turns "hiding and saying."

Hopscotch [K–2]

A hopscotch diagram is drawn on the floor or on a piece of suitable cloth or paper. In the spaces write the numbers from two through nine in any random order. Draw a small circle near the diagram, writing in it any selected number. Each pupil plays hopscotch by adding that number to each block as he jumps from block to block. Scores may be kept, if competitive games are to be played, or each child may keep cumulative scores for himself. The diagram may be drawn on the chalkboard, and the hopping done figuratively as children work at their seats. The number on the "stone" may be subtracted, as well as added.

Horse Race [K–2]

Choose as "horses" as many pupils as there are aisles. Give each seated pupil a number combination (addition, subtraction, multiplication, or division) to which he must know the answer if he is to play. The number combinations are the "hurdles" in the race. The "horses" start at a signal. Giving each answer allows the horse to proceed to the next hurdle. After an incorrect response, the pupil holding the combination puts his hand across the track (aisle) to restrain the horse until the correct answer is given. The first horse to answer all combinations on his track wins. Each pupil should have a chance to be a "horse."

Hull Gull [K–2]

A number of acorns, buttons, or similar objects are collected. Each player starts with an equal number of small objects. In his turn, one player places his hands behind his back and divides the number of objects between his two hands. When he brings one hand in front, the opposing player tries to guess the number of objects in the closed hand. If the guess is correct, he gets all of the buttons (or whatever is used). If he fails to guess correctly, the guesser must pay the other player the difference between the number of buttons in the fist and the number guessed. The player ending with the most buttons wins.

King of the Castle [K–2]

A "king" is chosen by lot (drawing numbers, for example). He then sits on his "throne" and members of his "court" (other pupils in the class) try to dethrone him by asking combinations that he doesn't know. If the king misses, he is dethroned. The pupil who asked the combination becomes the new king, if he knows the answer. If the asker misses, he is penalized by being put in jail, missing his next turn to ask a question.

Larks, Robins, and Swallows [K–2]

Number-combination cards are placed on the chalk tray. Cards containing the answers are distributed among the pupils at random. The pupils are then divided into "Larks," "Robins," and "Swallows." A bird fancier is appointed, and a "cage" located in a corner. When the caller says "Robins!", all Robins match answers to combination cards correctly and quickly. Any Robins who fail to find the combination fitting their answer cards are caught and caged. The answer cards are shuffled frequently to provide more practice. The caller alternates in calling different birds in a random order.

Making a Tree [K-2]

Draw the trunk of a tree on the chalkboard, with the number 10 on it. The pupils draw limbs as they give the answers to addition or subtraction combinations named by the teacher. For example, teacher says, "six plus what equals ten?" The first child to say "four" draws the limb and writes "6 + 4" on it. Any suitable number may be written on the trunk, as practice is needed.

More or Less [K-2]

Construct 30 cards of two different colors on which are arranged spot patterns of the numbers from 1 through 10. The pack of cards is shuffled and divided evenly between two players who place their cards face down in front of them. Each player exposes his top card. The one whose card contains the greatest number of spots scores the sum of (or difference between) the number of spots on the exposed cards. Scores are kept, and at the end of the game the one having the larger number wins.

Racing: Two by Two [K-2]

The teacher scatters the numbers from 2 through 20 on the chalkboard. Two pupils are selected to start and stand at the chalkboard with erasers and chalk in hand. Teacher calls out any number, as "5." The pair of pupils make addition or subtraction combinations using 5 (whether it is addition or subtraction is decided before the game starts) and write them on the board. The one who completes his combination first erases the original 5 from the numbers put up by the teacher, and takes his seat. The remaining pupil chooses another with whom to "race" and the game proceeds.

Ring Toss [K–2]

Use short lengths of broomstick nailed to small pieces of board Christmas-tree fashion, use milk bottles, or any similar upright pieces. Embroidery hoops, circles made of rope, or similar horseshoe-like items may serve as rings. Mark each upright as worth a given number of points, using both plus and minus values (if subtraction is to be practiced). Pupils toss hoops and keep scores as individuals or as teams.

Numbo [K–2]

Square cards are prepared, marked off into 25 smaller squares of one- or two-inch size. The 25 addition or subtraction combinations on which practice is desired (either whole numbers or fractions) are written in the squares. The cards are distributed to the pupils. The teacher calls a combination, then writes it on the chalkboard to give pupils time to find it on the card and cover it with a marker. The winner is the first player to have a vertical, horizontal, or diagonal line of markers, and calls "Numbo!"

Opposites and Answers [K–2]

Make 48 cards, eight inches long and four inches

wide. On 40 of them place the easy direct and reverse addition combinations. On eight write the answers from 3 to 10. Have each pupil draw a card. A pupil who has a combination card takes it to the front of the room and shows it to the class. The child holding the reverse form goes up to stand beside him. Then the pupil holding the card with the sum joins the first two, as: $3 + 2 = ?$, $2 + 3 = ?$, $? + ? = 5$.

Pairs [2–3]

Write these twenty addition combinations on cards:

6	7	8	9	5	6	7	8	9	8
+6	+7	+8	+9	+6	+7	+8	+9	+2	+3

9	7	8	9	7	8	9	8	9	9
+3	+4	+4	+4	+5	+5	+5	+6	+6	+6

Write the answers on twenty other cards. Mix all cards, and deal six to each of four players (other groups of four may play at the same time). Lay the remaining cards, in the set of 40, face down on the table. Pupils may draw cards throughout the game. For example, suppose the following were one player's cards:

8	9	6	18	6	13
+5	+3	+6		+7	

He may lay down one pair ($8 + 5$) or the other pair ($6 + 7$) with the same answer card, 13, as only one combination card and one answer card may be laid down at the same time. Then he may say, "I have $6 + 6$ and I want its answer, Mary." If she has it she must give it to him, and he then puts down another pair. He may continue calling for a combination card or an answer card until he fails to find its mate. Then he must draw. If successful, he draws again. If unsuccessful, he loses his turn. The first player to lay down all his cards in pairs is winner.

Kitten in the Corner [2–3]

Pupils form a circle. One pupil is chosen to be IT and is placed in the corner. Every child holds a number card, with each separate number being held by two children. IT announces a combination, as 7 and 5. The two children holding the number 12 must then change places, and the pupil who is IT tries to get the place of one of them during the shift.

Pony Track [2–3]

Two concentric circles are drawn on the chalkboard about a foot apart, with the diameter of the inner circle about one foot in length (making the diameter of the outer circle three feet). Number combinations are written around this "pony track." The pupil who answers all the combinations on paper at his seat first, or who gets the highest number correct, wins the race.

Relay Race [2–3]

Two teams are chosen. The teacher writes a number combination at each end of the chalkboard. At a signal, the first pupil in each team runs to the board, writes the answer, and writes a new combination. He then runs to his place and gives the chalk to the next pupil in line. That pupil goes forward and repeats the process. The line (or team) finishing first wins. If a pupil misses a combination, the next pupil in line tries to tell him *after* he returns to the line; he then goes back to the board to correct his error.

Sorting Mail [2–3]

The answers to various addition combinations (or subtraction, multiplication, or division, as appropriate) are placed on the chalkboard. Pupils are given a number of combination cards, which are treated as "mail" to be sorted. For example, if addition is being studied, the sum "14" may be given as an "address." In this case, the number cards containing $7 + 7$, $6 + 8$, $4 + 10$, and several other combinations, would be placed under the 14.

The Valentine Box [2–3]

All combinations that are known by the children (addition, subtraction, etc.) are written on cards and placed in a "Valentine Box." The pupils take turns drawing the cards out and giving the answers. If the answer to a card is correct, the child may keep the "Valentine." The object of the game is to collect a large number of "Valentines."

What Number? [2–3]

Make several cards with the numbers 1 through 10

for each pair of players. Get a supply of safety pins. Child A pins a number on the back of his partner, who then tries to determine the number, as follows: If the number 8 is pinned, Child B may say, "Is it 6?" Child B answers, "No, it is two more than 6." Child B then says, "It must be 8." Child B then changes roles with Child A. Game proceeds until the pair have used all their cards.

The Teacher [2–3]

Combinations being studied are written on cards (approximately 3″ × 5″ in size). These are shuffled, and the teacher starts by showing a card and calling on a pupil for the answer. If the answer is correct, the pupil keeps the card. The pupil holding the most cards when the stack has been used up becomes the "Teacher" for the next game.

Zooks [2–3]

Make sets of cards containing one each of the numbers 1 through 9. Deal all cards face down to the players. They should take turns showing one card at a time. When the sum of any two exposed cards is 10, the first pupil to say "Zooks" may collect all exposed cards. At the end of the game, when all cards have been turned up, the player with the most cards wins.

For practice in subtraction, the procedure is the same, except that a number to serve as the *difference* between any two exposed cards is announced, as 7.

Members of the class group form a line, or two lines, if team play is desired. The teacher collects a number of suitable problems and announces one to the first pupil in line. If he misses and the next pupil in line answers it, the two change places. If three pupils miss and the fourth answers, he changes place with the first pupil who missed. In team play, the problems shift from side to side, as well as down the row. In one-row play, the object is to get to the head of the line and stay there. In team play, points are awarded for correct answers, and the object is to gain more points than the other team.

Baseball Game [2–3]

The classroom group is divided into teams of approximately nine players each. The players make lists of four or five problems each, deciding on a difficulty rating for each problem as a "single," "double," "triple," or "home run." Teams at bat and teams in the field are chosen by lot. The team in the field "throws" the team at bat a question. If the player at bat answers it, he gets as many bases as the problem was rated. If he fails to answer, he is "out." Each team at bat gets three "outs." The game is scored by runs.

Checkers [2–3]

Construct a checkerboard. Write the difficult combinations in the different squares. Write the answers on small squares of cardboard to be used as "checkers." Each player is given the little answer squares for the combinations on his side of the board. The winner is the one who first covers all his combinations with the correct answers (without looking on the bottom side for the answers). The written answers on the squares are used for verification in case of challenge.

Factoring Practice [2–3]

The teacher selects a large number, of which the pupils are to find as many factors as they can in a given time. For example, the teacher may announce 480 or 360, and limit the time to four minutes. At the end of that time the pupils announce the number of factors they found, and the one with the largest number wins. The winner reads his list. Anyone who discovers a mistake in his list adds one point to his own score while the reader loses a point.

Simon Says [2–3]

Each pupil is given a card with a number on it, except one pupil who plays the role of Simon. All players put elbows on desks, hands in air and "thumbs up." The leader says, "Simon says twelve." Pupils whose cards are numbered 2, 3, 4, and 6 must put their thumbs down, since these are the numbers which divide 12 without a remainder. If "Simon says" nine, only those pupils whose numbers are 3 would put thumbs down. One point is scored for a correct answer, one point lost for an incorrect one. Number cards should be exchanged frequently.

Silent Multiplication   [3–4]

The products of the multiplication facts to be practiced are written on the chalkboard in random order. The class is divided into two teams. Teams choose leaders and each leader is given a pointer. The teacher holds up a combination card, such as 7 × 5. The player who first touches the tip of his pointer to the product of 7 × 5 on the chalkboard scores a point. The pointers are then passed to the next players, and so on in turn.

Rules can be adjusted so that players missing by pointing to the wrong answer are fined one point against the total score of their team.

Stepping Stones   [2–3]

Teacher draws two wavy lines about three feet apart to represent a "stream." Eight to twelve number combinations are written in oval enclosures about eight inches in diameter. These "stepping stones" are arranged so there are several routes from one shore to the other. Pupils choose routes and cross the stream by answering the combinations on each stone. Pupils watching must be alert for mistakes, causing those who make them to fall in the stream. They are "saved" by the pupil who then gives the correct combination.

The stream and stepping stones may be drawn on the

floor with chalk or on a roll of wide brown wrapping paper. The game may be used for all four processes, with whole numbers, and with fractions.

Telephone [2–3]

Each pupil is given a number. The teacher then says, "I am calling 2 and 4" (or any combination, addition or subtraction, as appropriate). The pupil who has the number 6 (if addition) or 2 (if subtraction) answers, as, "This is 6." The game continues in like manner.

Twenty Questions [2–3]

Twenty (or more or less, as desired) questions similar to those shown below are selected and printed on cardboard strips. The strips are shuffled and distributed. A pupil reads his question or number facts and selects someone to give the answer. The pupil who answers correctly asks the next question.

Examples:
Which is more, 7 + 4 or 3 + 6?
Which is more, a quarter or 3 dimes?
Which is less, 6 − 2 or 8 − 5?

Footprints [2–3]

An igloo and a trail of snowshoes leading to it are drawn on the board. Combinations are put on the snowshoes. Each child has a chance to see if he can answer all of the combinations correctly. If he can, he can go into the igloo. The teacher changes the combinations every time.

This game is on the same principle as the fireman game. The advantage here is that children like a change in games. Using footprints instead of a burning house makes it seem like two different games to them.

Call and Catch [2–3]

Here is a game that will give practice on combinations or multiplication facts. The first row of children are chosen to stand in a line. A dealer or a teacher throws the ball to the first child in the line. As she throws the ball, she calls out an arithmetic problem. The player must give the correct answer to the problem before he catches the ball. If he gives an incorrect answer or drops the ball, or gives the answer after he has caught the ball, he sits down and another player takes his place from the next row. The child who stays up the longest is the winner.

Arithmetic Tag [2–3]

This is a game that gives drill in the fundamentals of arithmetic. To play the game, the children form a circle. Two or three players volunteer to be in "mush pot," which is anywhere inside of the circle. Another person is chosen to be IT. He skips around the circle, stopping suddenly behind a player to challenge him with a problem. He may ask, for example, "Two plus four are how many?" The player who is being challenged must give the correct answer before someone in the mush pot does. If he succeeds, he becomes IT and goes skipping around the circle, stopping suddenly to challenge someone else. If he fails, he must exchange places with the winner in the mush pot. Players in the mush pot try to work their way out by calling out the answer ahead of the one being challenged.

A teacher must supervise this activity to make sure the problems the children use are appropriate. She can also list about fifty combinations on the board without the answers and let the children choose from them.

Ruler Relay [2–4]

Arrange the children's desks or tables into rows matched with each other. Each child puts his ruler on his desk. The teacher gives a set of slips to the first child in each row. The child takes one strip and passes the rest back to the child behind him. When each child gets his paper, he is to put it under the measuring side of the ruler so the paper can be measured lengthwise. As soon as the child has his paper and ruler ready and has made a mental note of the length of the paper, he stands to the right of his desk. The teacher then asks one person in the row what the paper measures.

A correct answer gives that team or row five points (the number of points can vary according to the incidental learning one might desire for addition and multiplication readiness). The slips are then to be passed to the front of the row, and the teacher gives each row new sets of slips. If a child reads the measurement incorrectly and gives the wrong answer, his team gets no points.

Circle the Clock [2–4]

The material needed is a chalkboard with as many circles on it as there are teams. The circles at the beginning of the game should have numbers written around the edge only. The number in the center, or the multiplier, is written in later. Numbers are put in different order around the circle. Multipliers may be varied to meet the needs of each child playing the game.

A pupil from each team goes to the board and faces the group. The teacher then writes in the multipliers. At a signal, the pupils face the board and write the product beside the outside numbers. After one minute or some other time limit, a signal is given and the chalk is put down. Teams check the results. One point is given if a pupil's answers are all correct. Then the answers are erased and the multiplier is changed for the next group.

Guess What I Am [2–4]

This game is quite elementary and would probably be used with second graders. It is basically concerned with the ability to estimate measurements.

The child who is IT pretends that he is a particular object in the room (a pencil, an eraser, etc.). After he whispers his identity to the teacher, the other children take turns asking him questions about his size, comparing it with other objects in the room. For example: "Are you taller than my chair?" "Are you as big as the bottle of paste?" A "yes" answer entitles the child to ask another question. The pupil who correctly guesses the identity of the object becomes IT next.

Ladder [3-6]

Draw a picture of a ladder on a piece of oak tag and supply three or four pupils with markers. Then shuffle a pile of cards containing number combinations (such as $9 + 4 = ?$; $17 - 6 = ?$; $8 \times 5 = ?$), and place them face down in the middle of the table so that pupils may take turns drawing cards, one at a time. If the correct answer is given, the pupil moves his marker one rung up the ladder. If he fails, he must try the same fact at his next turn. This game may also be played as a team game using a ladder drawn on the board. If a team member misses a question he must try to give the correct answer at the team's next turn. If he fails the second time, the next pupil tries to answer it. The first pupil or team to reach the top rung of the ladder wins.

This game can be used to review all the addition, subtraction, multiplication and division facts.

The Whole Story [3-4]

Pairs of numbers are written on cards. These are

shuffled and passed out. The teacher designates a pupil who names the numbers on his card, as 3 and 7, and "tells the whole story" of that pair of numbers. In this case, the whole story is: "Three 7's are 21, seven 3's are 21, 7's in 21 are 3, 3's in 21 are 7."

This game may be used for practice, with the teacher dictating the combinations.

Bowling [3–4]

Construct tenpins by using empty paper towel cylinders. Obtain a large, soft rubber ball. Place the tenpins in three rows at the back of the room. Let each tenpin count 2. The pupils take turns rolling the ball, determining the number of pins knocked down, and keeping score. If a child knocks down six pins, he should keep his score in this way: $6 \times 2 = 12$. When the game is over, the pupils read each other's scores for more practice.

Variations of this game may be used for division and for fractions, as well as whole numbers.

Paper Relay [3–4]

Five pupils for each of two teams are selected by lot. The teacher gives the first pupil on each team a multigraphed list of ten examples. Each pupil works one example and passes the paper to the next pupil. The last pupil in the row works two examples and starts the paper back up the row. Each player works a second example until the paper reaches the front of the row. The leader reads the examples. The team with the most correct answers wins.

Tick-Tack-Toe [3–4]

Draw a tick-tack-toe figure upon the chalkboard, one for each two pupils. Each space should contain two numbers to be multiplied (or divided). Give different colored chalk to each pupil. The aim is to get three products (or quotients) of one color in a row, as in the familiar "circle and cross" version of the ancient game.

The Traveler [3–4]

Two pupils are chosen by lot to start the game. A fact, such as 7×9, is announced by the teacher. The first of the pair to give the answer is the winner. The loser takes his seat, and the winner travels again. The point of the game is to see who can travel the farthest.

Around the Circle [3–4]

A circle is drawn on the chalkboard, with four or six diameters being drawn to divide the circle into sections. Appropriate fractions are written in the sections, with another fraction in the center. (A small circle is drawn at the center, and the intersections of the diameters erased, to leave a clear space for the center fraction.) This center fraction may be added to, subtracted from, multiplied by, or divided by the fractions in the sections. In a more advanced form, the fractions in the several sections of the circle may have different operation signs, to provide varied practice. Pupils may play as individuals or as teams.

Improved Baseball [4–6]

Used in the primary grades for addition and subtraction, this game may be adapted for use in grades five and six for practice in addition, subtraction, multiplication, and division of fractions.

Pupils are divided into teams, and the four corners of the room serve as "bases." As each team member "bats," he attempts to work three examples on the chalkboard (chosen by the teacher). If he fails to solve them, he is out. If worked correctly, the player goes to first base, and the next batter is "up." When three players miss, the other team comes to bat. Runs are scored by being "batted in," players "on base" moving around as fellow players work examples correctly.

Bank For Me [4–6]

Materials:
A bank statement, bank deposit slips, bank checks.

Have the children calculate the balance in an account from the bank statement alone. How will they be able to calculate it more correctly? Have children write checks and deposit imaginary amounts to this same account. At the end of the month, have the class make out another bank statement. A child appointed as a teller may check the bank statement. As the pupils become more proficient in making out the monthly statement, new accounts may be added to the bank.

Step Up [4–6]

One child stands behind another child's chair. The teacher gives a problem, and whoever supplies the right answer first goes on to the next person. This continues, with the children keeping score as to how many children each child passes as he goes around the room. This does not have to be scored, however. In case of a tie in saying the answer, the teacher gives the same two another chance at a different problem. This game can be utilized at any grade level with the various arithmetical processes.

Multiplication Relay [4–6]

Each row of children is a separate team. Assign a multiplication combination to each row. Each child multiplies the answer of the child in front of him by the multiplier in the combination assigned to his row. To give each child practice with both large and small combinations, start the paper at the back of the row every other time. The teacher checks each team's work before declaring the winner for the day. Each row could be assigned the same multiplication combination, and the first row to finish with the correct paper is the winner.

Golf

While pupils lay their heads on desks, with their eyes closed, the teacher or leader writes a story problem on the board. At the signal, "Go," all boys and girls look up, read the problem, and begin to work. As each pupil finishes, he raises his hand. The leader gives the first person to finish one point; the second, two points; and so on. These represent the "strokes" taken to make the first "hole." Each pupil records his score at the left side of his paper. Those who cannot finish the problem in a reasonable time are given an arbitrary number of "strokes" larger than those of other members of the group. The problem is then worked by a pupil at the board. Those who had incorrect answers must add as many "strokes" to their scores as were given to those who did not finish. Nine "holes" constitute a "round." The player with the lowest score wins.

Divide It

The dealer places a dealer's card (one with a division combination on it) on the table. The child putting the correct answer down first wins the dealer's card and takes it. The player with the most cards after the game is over is the winner.

How Much?

The materials needed are a box containing many slips of paper upon which are written an assortment of articles that convey certain measurements, with such quantities as "one-half gallon," "two-thirds of a yard," and so on.

The object of the game is for the person or persons selected as IT to reach into the box and take one of the slips. The IT (or ITs) then select properties from the prepared assortment and attempt to convey the message to the group or to their respective teams without using words. If the game is played by a single group, one IT is selected; and when a person from the group guesses IT's message, that person in turn becomes the new IT.

If the game is played with two teams, one IT from each team is selected. They both reach into the container at the same time, and they both try to convey their messages to their respective teams first. The team which first guesses IT's message wins a point. Team members take turns being IT.

Television Quiz Show [4–6]

Obtain a box into which the pupils can deposit their written questions. The questions, which are to be contributed in advance of the contest, should cover situations that the pupils encounter in their daily activities and that illustrate processes being learned. The teacher may go over all the problems submitted and keep those which he considers of value; he may appoint a committee from the class to do this under his supervision. The questions should be divided into three groups according to difficulty, and the easiest questions should be used for the less able pupils.

The class is divided into three groups according to ability, so that pupils compete against others at their own level of accomplishment. One group competes at a time. A pupil in the class, or the teacher, may be the master of ceremonies and asks the questions. A committee of three pupils may keep track of the scores. The group competing earns one point for each question or problem answered correctly.

Time Around the World [4–6]

The materials needed are paper, pencils, and chalkboard.

Arrange the players into three to five rows. One row is Tokyo, the second row is San Francisco, the third row is Denver, the fourth row is New York, the fifth row is London. On the chalkboard the teacher lists these cities:

2 A.M.	London
4 A.M.	Denver
8 P.M.	Tokyo
etc.	etc.

The players in each row are to calculate quickly their time corresponding to the other cities' time. The pupils stand up as they finish. The teacher checks the order in which each row completes the problems. The winning row is the one which finishes the quickest and with the highest number of correct answers. On succeeding rounds, the rows change names.

Addition Relay [4–6]

This exercise involves the addition of two 3-place

numbers and is designed to strengthen the process of addition.

Write a column of 3-place numbers on the board, and then divide the class into teams. At the signal to start, the first pupil on each team writes the first two numbers and totals them. He passes the paper to the next team member, who adds the third number on the board to the sum given by the previous pupil. This continues until all the numbers have been added. A sample column of figures and the work that would be done by the pupils in the row is shown below.

```
235 ⎫                   235
    ⎬ ————————→
192 ⎭                   192      1st pupil
                        ———
                        427
371 ——————————→         371      2nd pupil
                        ———
                        798
427 ——————————→         427      3rd pupil
                        ————
                        1225
863 ——————————→         863      4th pupil
                        ————
                        2088
537 ——————————→         537      5th pupil
                        ————
                        2625
```

The first team to finish with the correct answer is the winner.

Division Tables   [4–6]

This activity, which involves giving all the division facts for each table number, is a good method to foster the needed practice of the division process.

Write the dividends that occur in the table of division facts on 2″ × 3″ cards. Shuffle them and place them face down in the middle of a table. One of two players draws a card and gives all the even division facts for which the number in the card is a dividend. For most dividends there will be two facts (i.e., $45 \div 9 = 5$ and $45 \div 5 = 9$ for the dividend 45); for a few there will be but one fact (i.e., $81 \div 9 = 9$ for 81), and for others four facts ($18 \div 2 = 9$, $18 \div 9 = 2$, $18 \div 6 = 3$, and $18 \div 3 = 6$ for 18). Each player continues drawing cards and giving facts until he makes a mistake, at which point the other player takes over. The winner is the one with the most cards after the pile is depleted. Include several duplicate dividends on the cards for larger numbers of participants.

Caller [4–6]

Make a number of cards, each about eight inches square, cross-ruled into smaller squares. A zero (0) is written in the center square. The other spaces are filled with the products of multiplication tables currently being studied, as 0, 6, 12, 18, etc. These are in random order. On different sets of small colored squares (to cover the squares on the large card) the multiplication combinations are written, as $6 \times 0 = $?, $6 \times 1 = $?, etc. The table of 2's and table of 3's constitute one game, the 6's and 7's another, and so on. The materials mentioned above are for one game.

Let us consider the 6's and 7's as a game. The pupils place the large cards before them. On the left they place the small squares containing the multiplication combinations of 6, on the right those for the 7's. The Caller places his large card and small cards, blank side up, before him. All fill the free space in the center marked zero (0). It can be filled with the small square on which is written $7 \times 0 = ?$. The Caller picks up the small squares at random, reads the combination and product, then places the small square in the space that contains the answer. For example, the Caller picks up the square marked $6 \times 7 = ?$, reads "6×7 are 42" and places the square on the space marked 42 on the large card. Each pupil looks for his 6×7 card and places it on the space marked 42 on his own large card. The game continues until someone fills a line vertically, horizontally, diagonally, fills the four corners, makes a T, a Z, or a cross, as agreed upon in advance.

The Caller should state the answers to the combinations until most of the children are familiar with them. After they are well known, the combinations may be read without answers. Numbers should be read slowly, so pupils can keep up. Do not let anyone pick up a second square until all have placed the first one. The teacher should be Caller for the first few games, after which various pupils should take turns.

Math-tic [4–6]

Cut tagboard pieces $6'' \times 4''$ for pupils' cards, and $2\frac{1}{2}'' \times 1\frac{1}{2}''$ for tickets. Lay four tickets in a vertical row on the left side of the large card. Write an example or digital task on each ticket, and the answer opposite the ticket on the large card. Be certain that the same answer appears on several cards. Each pupil is given a large card with the answers and the teacher keeps the tickets. The teacher reads an example, and the pupils who have the answer on their cards raise their hands. The first one to raise his hand should be allowed to answer first. If he is incorrect, the teacher calls on the next pupil. When a pupil gives the correct answer, he is given the ticket to put on his card. When his card is filled with the four tickets, he calls "Math-tic" and drops out of the game. After three pupils have gotten "Math-tic," all exchange cards and start another game.

This game can also be used with whole numbers in the four basic processes in the early grades, as well as with decimal and percentage problems in the upper grades.

Fraction Change [4–6]

A number of fractions are written on cards. These are distributed to pupils. Pupils are then called upon, one at a time, to name the fraction on the card he holds, and to name an equivalent fraction in five seconds, or ten, or more, depending on the group). If he fails, his card goes to the first pupil who can name an equivalent fraction. The object of the game is to possess the most cards at the end of the game.

Many variations are possible. For example, a pupil may be asked to name as many equivalents as he can in ten seconds. The pupils take turns around the room (drawing a card out of the box as they are called on, so as to keep the preparation time even), and the pupil naming the longest list is declared the winner.

Estimation [4–6]

Have the first pupil on each of two teams estimate the length or weight of some object. Then measure or weigh it and give a point to the team of the pupil with the closer estimate. Continue in this fashion until every pair of opposing team members has estimated the length or weight of an object. The team with the most points wins.

Containers [4–6]

Choose teams and start the game by displaying a large jar partially filled with liquid. The first two team members compete by trying to estimate the amount of liquid in the jar. After each try, measure the amount of liquid using quart, pint, and ounce measuring units to determine which pupil has won a point for his team. The team with the most points at the end of the game wins.

Measure in Place [4–6]

Write on the board a scrambled list of linear measures and measures of weight and time (i.e., 13 ft.; 8:00; 3T.; 18 mi.; 2 lbs.; etc.). Also rule off two boxes, one for each team, containing three columns each, and head each set of columns: "Linear," "Weight," and "Time," respectively. Teams compete as in a relay race in sorting the list of measures into the appropriate columns as fast as possible. The first team to do so correctly wins.

Decimal Point [4–6]

Cut as many $7'' \times 11''$ cards as there are pupils. Print the numbers from 0 through 9 on the cards, putting only decimal points on two of the cards. Divide the class into two teams, each pupil having a card with a number or a decimal point. Each team should have one player with a decimal point on his card. When the teacher reads a number with a decimal, the pupils on each team holding cards with the numbers and the decimal point try to see which team can get to the front of the room and make the number first. The cards should be exchanged frequently, so that the same pupils do not have a disproportionate amount of the play. Scores are kept, the team with the highest score after a specified number of plays being the winner.

Bridging Numbers [4–6]

Ask all pupils to stand by their desks; then start the game by naming a single digit, such as 8. Pupils are to count, one after the other, by tens from that number. The first child would say "18," the second "28," the third "38," and so on. If a pupil gives a wrong response, he sits down, and the next pupil has a chance to say the number he missed. Pupils may also be asked to count by 20's (8, 28, 48, 68, etc.) by 9's, or other intervals.

Teams [4–6]

A good way to divide the class into teams for any

game is to shuffle and pass out cards containing sets of multiplication-fact products or division-table numbers. For example, you might pass out cards containing the products for the multiplication facts having 8 and 9 as multipliers. Omit the product 72 since it occurs in both tables. Duplicate products may be included in dividing into large teams. All pupils having a product belonging to the table of 8's (8, 16, 24, 32, etc.) gather on one side of the room, and those with products belonging to the table of 9's (9, 18, 27, 36, etc.) on the other side. Captains may be chosen automatically too, by agreeing before the game that the pupil receiving the card containing the 8 shall be one captain, and the pupil receiving the 9 shall be the other.

Teams may also be selected by passing out cards containing odd and even numbers. The pupil with the highest odd number and the one with the highest even number might be designated captains.

Guess [4–6]

A pupil-leader says he is thinking of a multiplication fact which has a certain product, say 24. Pupils try in turn to guess what the fact might be. If a pupil does not guess the fact the leader has in mind, the next pupil has a turn. This continues until a pupil guesses the fact, in which case the one doing so becomes the leader.

The game might also be played using dividends for even or uneven division facts. The pupil who says he is thinking of the uneven division fact having 39 for a dividend might have in mind $39 \div 6 = 6, R3$; a $39 \div 4 = 9, R3$; or $39 \div 9 = 4, R3$.

The Domino Sums [4–6]

Mix a set of dominoes and turn them face down in the center of a table. The game is played by two pupils who take turns selecting and displaying three dominoes at a time. The opposing player must tell the three numbers thus shown and then give their sum. If he does so correctly, he wins the three dominoes; otherwise, the dominoes must be turned face down again and mixed in with the others. The pupil with the most dominoes after all are used wins.

Captains Compete [4–6]

Choose several teams and captains for each. The captain stands in front of the row in which his team is seated, holding a card containing a number fact, such as $8 + 3 = 11$. The first team member must write on a sheet of paper a higher-decade example belonging to the same family, and then pass it to the next team member, who writes a different example in the same family. If the captain displays $8 + 3 = 11$, pupils may write $8 + 13 = 21$, $8 + 23 = 31$, $8 + 33 = 41$, etc. The game continues in this way, and the first team to finish wins.

Store Sales [4–6]

Start a class store in which empty cans and boxes brought from home are "purchased" by pupils. The storekeeper must correctly total the prices of goods purchased or the customer becomes the storekeeper.

The game may be varied by having a "Sale" in which all articles are four cents less than the price marked on each.

Division Steps [4–6]

Place two long-division examples on the board and choose two teams for a relay-type race. The first pupil goes to the board and divides, the second multiplies and compares, the third subtracts and compares, the fourth brings down, the fifth makes the second division, and so on. If a pupil notices a mistake in his team's work, he may work the example through from the start to make it correct. The first team to finish its example correctly is the winner.

I'm Thinking (2) [4–6]

The teacher or a pupil-leader says, "I'm thinking of a number. If you double it and add 7, you get 17. What is it?" (5). The first pupil to raise his hand and give the correct answer becomes the leader and continues with another combination.

Questions might also involve fractions: "I'm thinking of a mixed number. If you multiply it by 3, you get 100. What is it?" ($33\frac{1}{3}$). Decimals: "I'm thinking of a decimal. If you divide it by 10, you get 0.14. What is it?" (1.4). Or per cents: "I'm thinking of a per cent. If you subtract $2\frac{1}{2}\%$ from it, it equals $\frac{7}{8}$. What is it?" (90 %).

Divide the class into two teams and seat them in rows. Make up two sets of cards containing pictures of fractions. As the captain of each team displays his first card in front of his row, the first child on his team writes the fraction. The second writes his fraction and adds it to the previous fraction. The game continues until all pupils on a team finish with the correct answer.

PUZZLES

Puzzles should be an individual activity, and therefore it is recommended that they be duplicated and passed out to all children for individual seat work or after-school enrichment practice.

The prime objective of puzzle activities is to develop thinking power and, as such, no time limit should be set upon them. Arithmetic puzzles should be used as a before-school activity, or as a culminating activity to the formal arithmetic lesson. Children should be encouraged to do all the arithmetical computation on the puzzle paper itself. In this way the teacher can check and see what thinking process went on to obtain the answer. Many perceptive teachers can identify computational deficiencies by use of the arithmetic puzzle.

The puzzle affords the child the opportunity to demonstrate his understanding of various numerical concepts and operations. Puzzles like the magic star, the magic square, the magic wheel, and crossword puzzles constitute the types most favored by children.

PART FOUR

PUZZLES

Connect the numbers and you will discover
what animal is hiding among the trees.

153

Can you tell what comes next in each of the following patterns? Supply the next number, symbol, or drawing, as the case may be.

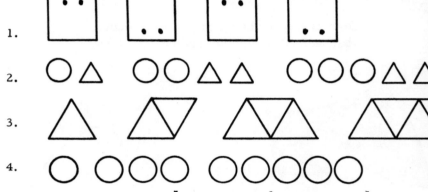

1.

2.

3.

4.

5.

6.   3,   7,   11,   15,   19,____, ____, ____

7.   360,   180,   90, ____

8.   6 in.,   1 ft.,   1 in.,   1 ft.,   8 in., ____

9.   3600,   1800,   600,   150,____

10. A_1 Z_{26} B_3 Y_{24} C_5 X_{22}____, ____

Answers:
        6. 23,   27,   31
        7. 45
        8. 1 foot
        9. 75
        10. D_7 , W_{20}

Solve all the examples. Color in all the shapes with an
answer of four (4) to find an object.

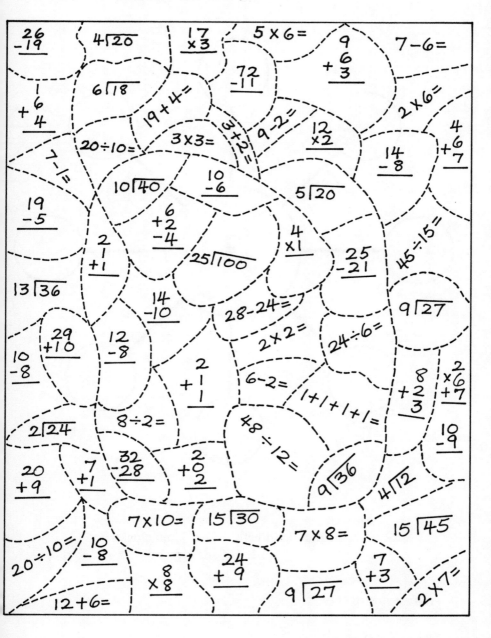

Put the numerals from 1 through 8 only once in the outside circles to make each line of numbers total *12*.

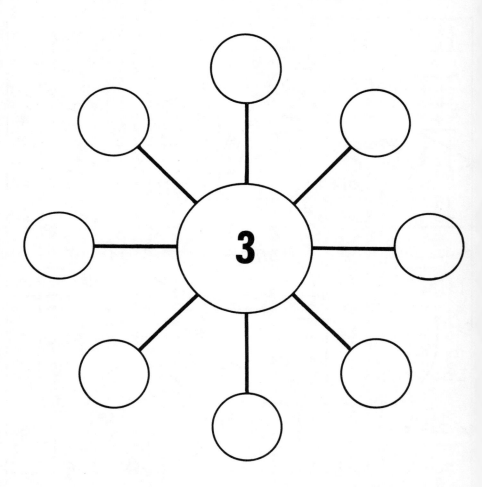

Answer:
Beginning directly above 3 and clockwise:
1, 2, 4, 6, 8, 7, 5, 3

How Many?

Write in the number answers. They will add up to 38.

How many:
    1. toes on one foot?   _____
    2. wings on a bird?   _____
    3. nickels in a dollar?   _____
    4. wheels on a car?   _____
    5. days in a week?   _____
                Total   _____

Add-a-Trail [2–4]

1	2	5	4	2
2	4	3	1	2
3	1	4	2	3
5	5	1	3	1
4	3	2	4	6

68

SOLUTION

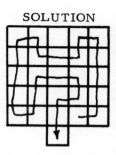

Draw a special trail to the answer in the bottom box of the puzzle. This trail will be a continuous line connecting some of the numbers in the puzzle. It must end at the number in the bottom box, and the numbers in the trail must add up to the total in the bottom box. You can use each box only once.

Use number line

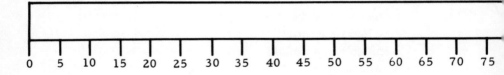

Begin With	Size of Interval	Number of Moves	End With	Answers
0	2½	5		12½
2	½	9		4½
3½	2½	4		11½
13½	1¼		19¾	6¼
37		19	46½	9½

Measurements [4–6]

Start with a gross, multiply by a dozen, divide by the number of inches in a yard, subtract a century, add a pair, and subtract a week. What measurement does your answer suggest?

Mental Arithmetic [4–6]

Take a number, double it, add (any number instructor wants), divide by 2, subtract original number. Answer will always be ½ the number given by the instructor.

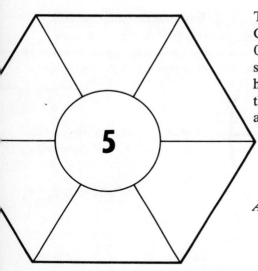

This is a magic wheel. Can you put the numerals 0, 1, 2, 3, 4, 5 in the spaces so that no matter how the wheel is read, three numerals across will add up to 10?

Answer: Beginning above the 5 and clockwise:
0, 3, 1, 5, 2, 4

Magic Star [2–4]

Fill in each circle with a numeral, so that no matter which line you add, the sum of the four numerals will be 12.

Use numerals: 1, 2, 3, 4, 5

Answer: Begin with the circle in front of the 3 and clockwise:

4, 2, 5, 3, 1

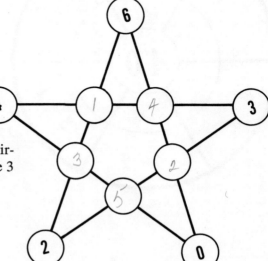

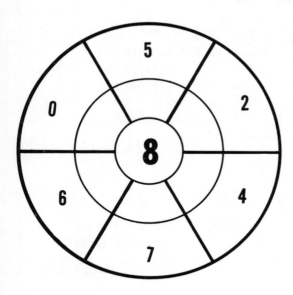

Here is some number fun with circles. Find the missing addends. The sum must equal 8.

Answer: Begin above the 8 and go clockwise:

3, 6, 4, 1, 2, 8

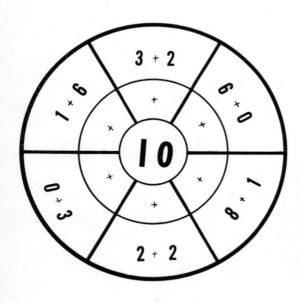

Write another combination so that the sum of the four addends will be 10.

Answer: Begin above the 10 and go clockwise:

4 + 1, 2 + 2, 0 + 1, 3 + 3, 7 + 0, 1 + 2

The five pieces in this puzzle will form a perfect square if they are cut out and put together correctly. The puzzle can be solved by finding the sums along the edges. When all the answers are found, match equal answers on different pieces of squares and the puzzle will be solved.

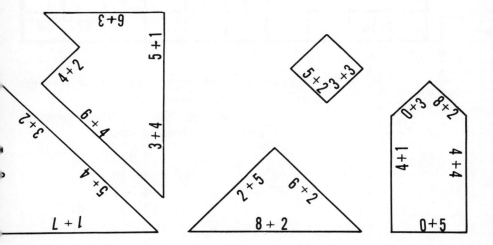

Solution:

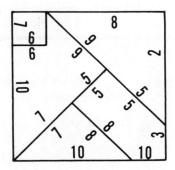

Fill in the missing numbers in order to discover numbers that fit into patterns.

5	8	7				10		14	15
2	4	5	3	7		6	5		
3	4	2	4	6	9		8		
6	16	10			36			49	56

Answer: Add the two middle rows to get the top line.
Multiply the two middle rows to get the bottom line.

Across: 7, 13, 13, 13
4, 7, 6
4, 7, 7
12, 42, 24, 40

3	4	2	6	5			8	7	2
8	8	10			12	14		14	15
5	4	8	8	7	9	6	3		

Answer: Subtract top row from second row to get last row.

Across: 3, 8
14, 12, 11
7, 13

Find the equal total for each
row in this magic square.

2	9	
	5	3
6	1	

Answer: 15

4
7
8

This one is a little harder.
Start by adding up the
third column.

	2	3	13
5	11	10	
9		6	
	14	15	

Answer: 34

16
8
7, 12
4, 1

Can you do this one too?

19		13	
	27	20	15
26	11	18	
	22	25	

Answer: 76

16, 28
14
21
17, 12

The following numbers appeared on a chalkboard:

4   5   6   7   8   9

The teacher said she could guess the right number if anyone wishes to choose one.

Her directions were:

Choose any number. Multiply it by 6. Add 12. Divide by 2, and write your answer on a piece of paper.

She then looked at the paper and correctly named the number initially chosen.

Solution: Divide the number written by 3 and subtract 2 from the quotient. That is the original number.

The Funny 9 [3–6]

Look at this multiplication table of 9. Do you see a pattern?

$$1 \times 9 = 9$$
$$2 \times 9 = 18$$
$$3 \times 9 = 27$$
$$4 \times 9 = 36$$
$$5 \times 9 = 45$$
$$6 \times 9 = 54$$
$$7 \times 9 = 63$$
$$8 \times 9 = 72$$
$$9 \times 9 = 81$$

The ones column in the products *decrease* in order.

The tens column in the products *increase* in order.

The *sum* of each product totals 9.

I Can Read Your Mind

Think of a number.

Double it.

Add 10.

Divide by 2.

Subtract from the total the original number.

Answer:　　is always 5

The Answer is Always the Same [2–6]

Take any number of 3 digits.	843
Reverse it and subtract the smaller number.	−348
	495
Reverse answer and add.	+594
	1089

Answer:　　is always the same:　　1089

Find the Mystery Number [2–6]

Use each number only once.
Cross out the number when it is used.

1	2	3
4	5	6
7	8	9

1. two numbers whose sum is 3.

2. two numbers whose sum is 8.

3. two numbers whose sum is 12.

4. two numbers whose sum is 15.

5. The number that is left is the mystery number 7.

Solve the arithmetic examples first, then decipher the message below by putting the letter which corresponds to the number in the message.

$A = 15 + 3 - 2$ (16) $K = 17 - 6 + 6$ (17)
$B = 4 - 3 + 1$ (2) $L = 12 + 11 - 20$ (3)
$C = 7 + 1 + 1$ (9) $M = 14 + 2 - 1$ (15)
$D = 9 - 6 + 2$ (5) $N = 7 + 2 - D$ (4)
$E = 14 + 11 - 5$ (20) $O = 18 + 9 - L$ (24)
$F = 11 + 4 + 3$ (18) $P = 6 + 2 - 1$ (7)
$G = 7 - 5 + 6$ (8) $Q = 19 - L - 3$ (13)
$H = 1 + 8 + 1$ (10) $R = 20 + D + 1$ (26)
$I = 26 - 3 - 2$ (21) $S = 6 + P - 7$ (6)
$J = 13 - 3 + 1$ (11) $T = K + 4 - 2$ (19)

$U = 17 - S + 1$ (12)
$V = S + 4 + 12$ (22)
$W = H + C - D$ (14)
$X = 20 + 1 - B$ (19)
$Y = 25 - 1 + 3$ (27)
$Z = 25 + 1 - 25$ (1)

W	E	L	C	O	M	E
14	20	3	9	24	15	20

T	O		T	H	I	R	D
19	24		19	10	21	26	5

G	R	A	D	E
8	26	16	5	20

Multiplication Crossword Puzzle [4–6]

This is a tougher crossword puzzle. Figure out the examples shown opposite and fill in the empty spaces in the puzzle.

Across

(a)   28
    × 19

(d)   107
    × 84

(h)   49
    × 56

(j)   32
    × 23

(k)   234
    × 25

(l)   13
    × 32

(m)   382
    × 18

(o)   367
    × 18

(r)   125
     × 4

(s)   733
     × 9

(v)   31
    × 24

(w)   304
    × 26

(x)   192
    × 15

(y)   32
    × 19

Down

(a)   210
    × 25

(b)   27
    × 14

(c)   49
     × 5

(e)   1083
     × 9

(f)   297
    × 28

(g)   433
     × 2

(i)   580
     × 7

(n)   963
     × 9

(o)   72
    × 84

(p)   144
    × 42

(q)   486
    × 18

(r)   44
    × 13

(t)   149
     × 4

(u)   75
    × 12

Answer:

<table>
<tr><td colspan="3">Across</td><td>a</td><td>b</td><td>c</td><td></td><td>d</td><td>e</td><td>f</td><td>g</td><td colspan="2">Down</td></tr>
</table>

Across		Down
a. 532		a. 5250
d. 8988		b. 378
h. 2744		c. 245
j. 743		e. 9747
k. 5850		f. 8316
l. 416		g. 866
m. 6876		i. 4060
o. 6606		n. 8667
r. 500		o. 6048
s. 6597		p. 6048
v. 744		q. 8748
w. 7904		r. 572
x. 2880		t. 596
y. 608		u. 900

Crossword Puzzle [4–6]

Try this crossword puzzle. Write the word out for each of the steps:

Across

1. two + two

4. 6 + 4

6. 10 − 1

Down

2. 3 − 2

3. 10 − seven

4. 6 − 5 + 1

5. 4 plus 2

A Surprise

Write a correct numeral and a letter.

d	g	k	o	r	w
⚁	⚂	⚃	⚃	⚅	⚅○

7 - 4 = ☐ ○   5 + 2 = ☐ ○

2 + 3 = ☐ ○   8 - 3 = ☐ ○

9 - 4 = ☐ ○   2 + 4 = ☐ ○

10 - 8 ☐ ○   10 - 6 = ☐ ○

Answer:

3 - g
5 - o
5 - o
2 - d

7 - w
5 - o
6 - r
4 - k

Casting Out Nines

Division is really a short cut for subtraction. If we wish to divide 43 by 9 we use this conventional method:

$$9\overline{)43}^{\;4\ r7}$$

or we can arrive at the same quotient by casting out nines, thusly:

$$43 - 9 = 34, \quad 34 - 9 = 25, \quad 25 - 9 = 16,$$
$$16 - 9 = 7r$$

4 nines cast   7 remainder

Strange patterns appear in the multiplication operation. Look at the following:

$$\begin{array}{r} 12345679 \\ \times \qquad 9 \\ \hline 111111111 \end{array}$$

$$\begin{array}{r} 12345679 \\ \times \qquad 18 \\ \hline 98765432 \\ 12345679 \\ \hline 222222222 \end{array}$$

$$\begin{array}{r} 12345679 \\ \times \qquad 27 \\ \hline 86419753 \\ 24691358 \\ \hline 333333333 \end{array}$$

To get 4's, multiply by 36.
To get 5's, multiply by 45.
To get 6's, multiply by 54.
To get 7's, multiply by 63.
To get 8's, multiply by 72.
To get 9's, multiply by 81.

Do you notice that the multipliers all equal 9?

Working With 8's   **[4–6]**

$$9 \times 9 + 7 = 88$$

$$98 \times 9 + 6 = 888$$

$$987 \times 9 + 5 = 8888$$

Can you do the rest?

Working With 4's [4–6]

Can you write 16 fours so that their sum is equal to 1000? Here is a hint:

$$444 + 444 = 888 \qquad \text{What is the rest?}$$

Solution:

$$444 + 444 + 44 + 44 + 4 + 4 + 4 + 4 + 4 + 4$$
$$= 1000$$

Products of One [4–6]

Will all these products be ones? Let's find out.

	Answer:
$1 \times 9 + 2 =$	11
$12 \times 9 + 3 =$	111
$123 \times 9 + 4 =$	1,111
$1234 \times 9 + 5 =$	11,111
$12345 \times 9 + 6 =$	111,111
$123456 \times 9 + 7 =$	1,111,111
$1234567 \times 9 + 8 =$	11,111,111
$12345678 \times 9 + 9 =$	111,111,111

An Arithmetic Crossword Puzzle [4–6]

	Across		Down
a.	$7 \times 8 =$	a.	$500 + 70 + 4$
b.	9 hundreds,	b.	$9 \times 8 - 6$
	2 tens, 3 ones	d.	$3 \text{ tens} - 1$
f.	$700 + 60 + 5$	e.	92×4
i.	8 twelves	h.	five thousand, three
j.	3 dozen		hundred and seventy
l.	$1000 + 700$	k.	8×8
	$+ 40 + 2$	l.	$\to 12$
n.	DCCCXXX	m.	2 feet, plus 3 inches
o.	Ten 7's $+ 2$		$=$ _____ in

Answer:

	Across		Down
a.	56, b. 923, f. 765	a.	574, b. 66, d. 29
i.	96, j. 36, l. 1,742	e.	368, h. 5,370, k. 64
n.	830, o. 72	l.	13, m. 27

Thinking Crossword [4–6]

Complete this crossword puzzle by writing the numbers 1 to 13 inclusive in the empty boxes.

They must total the exact amount shown at the ends of the eleven rows.

Answer: Across from the top:

3, 8, 5, 7, 12, 9, 1, 11, 13, 6, 4, 10, 2

Fish Weight   [4–6]

Guess how many pounds this fish weighs. Then add the single numbers to see if you guessed correctly.

Answer: 44 pounds

Fill In Number   [4–6]

Fill in the three blank columns in each box. The first column in each box is done for you.

8			
16			
22			
11			
3			

Write a number.

Multiply it by 2.

Add 6.

Divide by 2.

Subtract the first number.

What answer do you get every time?

4			
8			
18			
9			
5			

Write a number.

Multiply it by 2.

Add 10.

Divide by 2.

Subtract the first number.

What answer do you get every time?

	Answer:		*Answer:*
a34	a = 2	a46	a = 7
567	b = 5	× 35b	b = 2
4bc	c = 9	14c2	c = 9
+201		3d30	d = 7
d497	d = 1	2238	
		2e2f9g	e = 6, f = 5, g = 2

```
  9 3 5 2 8 4    Answer:
−   a b c d e    a through e is "9"
  ─────────
  f 3 5 2 8 5    f = 8
```

Puzzle Matching Numbers   [2–4]

Cut cardboard strips 4″ long by 1½″ wide.

In the left-hand corner of each strip, draw a semi-concrete number grouping. In the right-hand corner, print the corresponding abstract number. Cut each strip into two jig-saw puzzle pieces.

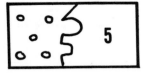 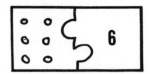

The object of these puzzles is for the child to recognize the grouping accurately, and to fit the pieces together, thus matching the semi-concrete grouping with the abstract number symbol.

ABCDEFGHIJKLMNOPQRSTUV
WXYZ

Answer:

First Word

8	7	16	25	30
+5	−2	+ 2	− 7	− 5

Merry

Second Word

10	4	10	13	15
− 7	+4	+ 8	− 4	+ 4

35	10	5	17
−15	+ 3	−4	+ 2

Christmas

Third Word

8	6	14
−7	+8	−10

And

Fourth Word

20
−19

A

Fifth Word

6	3	19	8	19
+2	−2	− 3	+8	+ 6

Happy

Sixth Word

19	9	18
− 5	−4	+ 5

New

Seventh Word

29	4	9	37
− 4	+1	−8	−19

Year

Key: A is 1, B is 2, C is 3 . . . . . . Z is 26.

Write the figures 1 to 9 in these nine boxes in such a way that the *sum* of the numbers on each of the three sides of the triangle equals 20.

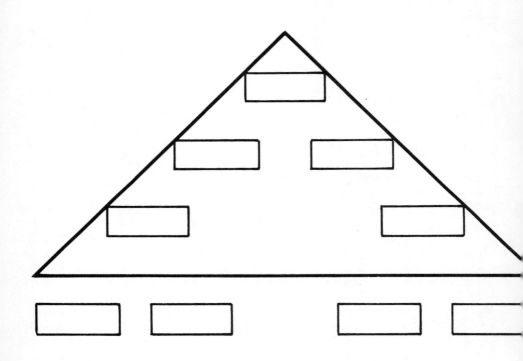

Answer: (top) 5; (left side) 3, 8; (right side) 2, 7; (bottom) 4, 1, 9, 6

Fill in the Missing Numbers [4–6]

Fill in the missing numbers in the square on page 177.

	□	○	△	◇
A	3	1		
B		4		16
C	5		8	
D	6			36
E	7		7	

KEY

$$□ + ○ = △$$
$$□ × ○ = ◇$$

Answer:

A. 4, 4
B. 4, 8
C. 3, 15
D. 0, 0
E. 0, 0

Placing Numerals   [4–6]

I

In each circle place one of the following numbers:

1 2 3 4 5 6 7 8 9

The sum of the three numbers in each line must be *15*.

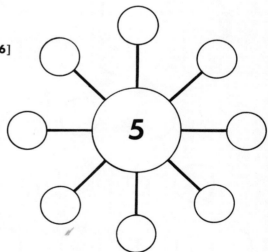

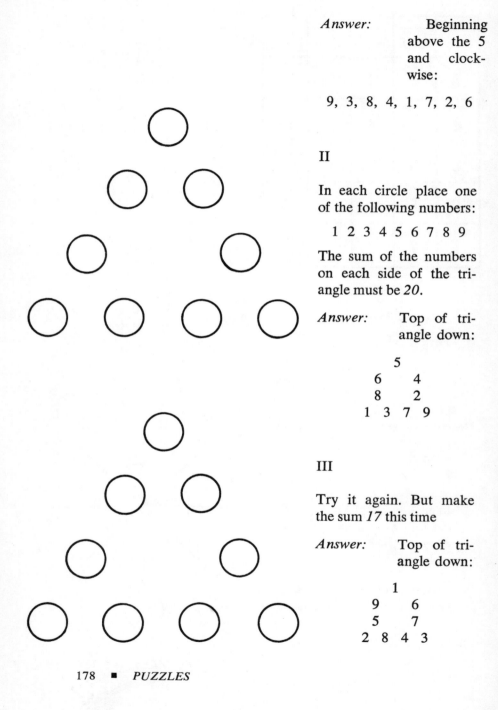

II

In each circle place one
of the following numbers:

1 2 3 4 5 6 7 8 9

The sum of the numbers
on each side of the tri-
angle must be *20*.

Answer: Top of triangle down:

```
        5
     6     4
     8     2
   1  3  7  9
```

III

Try it again. But make
the sum *17* this time

Answer: Top of triangle down:

```
        1
     9     6
     5     7
   2  8  4  3
```

1. Both numerator and denominator of a fraction may be divided by the same number without changing the value of the fraction.

2. When a fraction represents an indicated division, both divisor and dividend may be multiplied by the same number without changing the value of the fraction:

Thus, $\dfrac{3}{4} = \dfrac{3 \times 3}{3 \times 4} = \dfrac{9}{12}$

1. $\dfrac{3}{4} \overline{/6}$

2. $\dfrac{3}{4} \times \dfrac{4}{3} \overline{/6 \times \dfrac{4}{3}}$

3. $1/8$ or 8

Similarly,

$$4/8 = 2 \times 4 \overline{/2 \times 8}$$

So,

$$6 \div \dfrac{3}{4} = \dfrac{3}{4} \overline{/6} = \dfrac{3}{4} \times \dfrac{4}{3} \overline{/6 \times \dfrac{4}{3}}$$

Because $\dfrac{3}{4} \times \dfrac{4}{3} = 1$

$\dfrac{3}{4} \times \dfrac{4}{3} \overline{/6 \times \dfrac{4}{3}} = 1 \overline{/6 \times \dfrac{4}{3}}$

1. $6 \div \dfrac{3}{4}$

2. $6 \times \dfrac{4}{3} \div \dfrac{3}{4} \times \dfrac{4}{3}$

3. $6 \times \dfrac{4}{3} \div 1$ or $6 \times \dfrac{4}{3}$

$1 \overline{/6 \times \dfrac{4}{3}} = \boxed{6 \times \dfrac{4}{3}}$

$1/8 = 8$

3. Multiplying the divisor by its *reciprocal* changes it to one. Two numbers are reciprocals when their product is one.

   For instance, the reciprocal of 2 is ½, the reciprocal of ½ is 2, the reciprocal of ¾ is ⁴⁄₃.

4. The solution can be shortened to include only the step in which the dividend is multiplied by the reciprocal of the divisor:

$$\text{Thus: } 6 \div \frac{3}{4}$$

$$6 \times \frac{4}{3} = 8$$

Working With Different Bases

Base Eight

(8)	1	2	3	4	5	6	7	10
(10)	1	2	3	4	5	6	7	8

In base eight: 234 means   2 sixty-fours (8×8)
                                   3 eights
                                     4 ones

In base ten: 234 means   2 hundreds
                                     3 tens
                                     4 ones

In base eight: 120 means   (right to left)
                                     no ones
                                     2 eights
                                     1 sixty-four

Changing 234 from base eight to base ten:

$$
\begin{aligned}
4 &= 4 \text{ ones} &&= 4 \\
3 &= 3 \text{ eights} &&= 24 \\
2 &= 2 \text{ sixty-fours} &&= 128 \\
\hline
&&& 156
\end{aligned}
$$

Changing 156 from base ten to base eight:

8 156
8 19 with remainder of 4 ones
   2 with remainder of 3 eights

Base Two   Use symbols 1 & 0 (computer off/on
           thinking)

1 = 1	5 = 101
2 = 10	6 = 110
3 = 11	7 = 111
4 = 100	8 = 1000

Base Twelve   (anything above ten . . . we use
         letters or new symbols)

(12) 1 2 3 4 5 6 7 8 9 t e 10

(10) 1 2 3 4 5 6 7 8 9 10 11 12

Base Ten	Base Two	Base Eight	Base Twelve
1	1	1	1
2	10	2	2
3	11	3	3
4	100	4	4
5	101	5	5
6	110	6	6
7	111	7	7
8	1000	10	8
9	1001	11	9
10	1010	12	t
11	1011	13	e
12	1100	14	10
13	1101	15	11
14	1110	16	12
15	1111	17	13

MATH
EQUIPMENT

Most teachers are resourceful and are continually gathering supplementary materials to enhance their teaching lessons. Inasmuch as motivation, with emphasis on intrinsic values, is of such great importance to elementary school children, teachers are constantly looking for new approaches, new avenues of experience, and new sources of ideas to promote this motivation.

This section contains some of the classroom objects that teachers have collected for the teaching of arithmetic. It also lists some of the commercial games that can be purchased inexpensively for promoting arithmetic inquiry. There is a listing of monthly educational materials and reprints that can be obtained free by all teachers. Many of these curriculum materials contain excellent ideas for improving arithmetic teaching.

Finally, for those teachers who want to explore the new approaches to arithmetic, there is an index of addresses of some of the new "math plans" which have gained popularity in the past few years.

PART FIVE

EQUIPMENT

Useful Classroom Materials for Teaching Arithmetic

Teachers should strive to collect the following classroom materials as supplemental and enrichment devices for the teaching of arithmetical concepts and operations. Many of these materials can be contributed by the children.

Abacus
Acorns and acorn cups
Adding machine
Advertisements
Atlas
Attendance slips and reports

Baseball batting averages
Beads (for stringing)
Beans (various types)
Blocks (various sizes)
Bottles (various sizes)
Boxes (many shapes and sizes)
Bottle caps
Buttons

Calendars
Cans (glass, tin)
Cash register (toy)
Chalkboard (graph, ruled)
Checkers and board
Circles (wood, cardboard)
Clock (alarm)

Clock dial
Clothes pins (spring type)
Compass (drawing)
Compass (navigational)
Cookbook
Counting board
Cubic measure (paper or wood)

Dials (meter type)
Discs (fractional)
Dice
Display cards
Dominoes
Draftsman's triangle

Egg cartons
Egg timer

Flannel board
Fraction chart
Fractional part models

Globes

Graph Paper
Graphs (bar, circle, picture, line)

Height and weight charts
Hemisphere models
Hourglass (egg timer)

Invoices

Jigsaw puzzles

Level (carpenter's)
Library time return slips
Linoleum designs

Maps (road and relief)
Marbles
Measuring unit sets
Metric Table
Meter stick
Micrometer
Money (toy and real)
Money Order blanks
Muffin tins

Notes (bank)
Number line

Odometer

Pairs of objects
Paper (folded in squares, triangles)
Paper plates
Pedometer
Pegboard
Plastic plate (divided)
Place value chart

Playing cards
Poker chips
Price lists
Prism
Protractor
Promissory notes

Recipes
Rulers
Rectangles

Scales
Scissors
Score cards
Seeds
Speedometer
Slide rule
Spheres
Spools
Square measure (inch, yard)
Squares (L and T)
Stamps (sales, bonus, postage)
Sticks (colored counting)
Sticks (tongue depressers)
Stop watch
Sundial

Tape measure
Telephone (toy and real)
Telephone book
Thermometer (all types)
Tickets (theater and other types)

Wheel

Yardstick

Commercial Companies Offering Arithmetical Enrichment Aids for Teachers

Teaching aids and enrichment devices in arithmetic can be obtained by writing to the following commercial and publishing companies. Write for a free catalog.

Teachers Publishing Corporation
23 Leroy Avenue
Darien, Connecticut 06820

Ideal School Supply Company
8312 South Birkhoff Avenue
Chicago, Illinois 60620

LaPine Scientific Company
South Buckhout Street
Irvington, New York

The Learning Center
Creative Playthings
Princeton, New Jersey

Science Research Associates
259 East Erie Street
Chicago 11, Illinois

Instructo Products
1635 N. 55th Street
Philadelphia 31, Pennsylvania

Hayes School Publishing Company
201 Rebecca Avenue
Wilkinsburg, Pennsylvania

Milton Bradley Department
School Department
Springfield, Massachusetts 01101

School Service Company
4233 Crenshaw Boulevard
Los Angeles 8, California

Scott Plastics Company
P.O. Box 2840
Sarasota, Florida

Richards Research Associates
135 Southcote Road
Riverside, Illinois

Milliken Publishing Company
611 Olive Street
St. Louis 1, Missouri

Creative Publishing House
Oxford, Ohio

Holt, Rinehart and Winston Company
383 Madison Avenue
New York, New York

Free Monthly Arithmetic Publications
Available to Teachers

Send your name and school address on school stationery to the following companies for free monthly publications on topical arithmetic features:

The Editor, *STA Mathematics Forum*
Scott Foresman Company
433 East Erie Street
Chicago, Illinois 60611

Miss Meanne Truex, Editor
Education Today
Charles Merrill Company
1300 Alum Creek Drive
Columbus 16, Ohio

Miss Elizabeth Cronin, Editor
Elementary School Notes
Ginn and Company
Statler Building
Boston 17, Massachusetts

Editor, *Teaching Trends*
Scott Foresman Company
433 East Erie Street
Chicago, Illinois 60611

Service Report for Schools
Webster Publishing Company
St. Louis, Missouri

Elementary Teacher Monographs
Row, Peterson and Company
Evanston, Illinois

Curriculum Letters
School Service Department
Wesleyan University
Middletown, Connecticut

Educational Journals Containing Practical Teaching Aids and Articles in Arithmetic

The Grade Teacher
Teachers Publishing Corporation
23 Leroy Avenue
Darien, Connecticut

The Instructor
Owen Publishing Company
Dansville, New York

The Arithmetic Teacher
1201 Sixteenth Street
N.W. Washington 6, D.C.

Education Magazine
Bobbs-Merrill Publishing Company
4300 West 62 Street
Indianapolis 6, Indiana

Elementary School Journal
University of Chicago
5835 Kimbark Avenue
Chicago 37, Illinois

The NEA Journal
National Education Association
1201 Sixteenth Street
N.W. Washington 6, D.C.

The Scholastic Teacher
900 Sylvan Avenue
Englewood Cliffs, New Jersey

The Education Digest
330 Thompson Street
Ann Arbor, Michigan

Educational Summary
100 Garfield Avenue
New London, Connecticut

Mathematics Student Journal
1201 Sixteenth Street
N.W. Washington 6, D.C.

School Life
U.S. Department of Education
Washington 25, D.C.

Teacher's Directory of Information
for New Math Programs

Write to these addresses for information and samples of programs dealing with the "new math" approaches.

National Council of Teachers of Mathematics
1201 Sixteenth Street
N.W. Washington 6, D.C.

The Cuisenaire Company
9 Elm Avenue
Mount Vernon, New York

National Science Foundation
1951 Constitution Avenue
N.W. Washington 6, D.C.

University of Illinois Committee on Mathematics
University of Illinois
1207 West Springfield Avenue
Urbana, Illinois

School Mathematics Study Group
Stanford University
Stanford, California

Dr. Robert B. Davis
Madison Mathematics Project
Webster College
Webster Groves 19, Missouri

Dr. David A. Page
University of Illinois Arithmetic Project
1207 W. Stoughton Avenue
Urbana, Illinois

University of Maryland Mathematics Project
University of Maryland
College Park, Maryland

Dr. Patrick Suppes
Sets and Numbers Project
Stanford University
Stanford, California

Encyclopedia Brittanica Press
Wirtz-Botel Sawyer Math Workshop
425 North Michigan Avenue
Chicago, Illinois

Commercial Arithmetic Games That Can be Used in the Classroom

Aritho (Fundamental operations)

Psychological Services
4502 Stanford Street
Chevy Chase, Maryland

Attaboy's Number Puzzle Game (Fundamental operations)

The Attaboy Co.
Wichita Falls, Texas

Bingo (Number recognition)

Various manufacturers.

Buyer's Mark-Up Calculator (Decimals and percentage)

The Accounting Press
Chicago, Illinois

Chuck-O-Luck (Addition and subtraction)

    E. S. Lowe Co.
    New York, New York

Contact (Addition and multiplication)

    Parker Brothers
    Salem, Massachusetts

Counting House (Number values and combinations)

    Playskool Manufacturing Co.
    Chicago, Illinois

Dolch Number Games (Fundamental operations)

    Garrard Press
    Urbana, Illinois

Dominoes (Number recognition, grouping)

    Various manufacturers.

Domino Blocks (Number recognition, combinations, and separations)

    A. C. Gilbert Co.
    New Haven, Connecticut

Economo (Number recognition)

    Milton Bradley Co.
    Springfield, Massachusetts

First Counting Board (Number recognition and counting)

    Educational Playthings
    Sandusky, Ohio

Flinch (Number recognition and sequence)

    Parker Brothers
    Salem, Massachusetts

Go to the Head of the Class (Counting)

Milton Bradley Co.
Springfield, Massachusetts

Hoop-O-Loop Hunting Game (Adding and subtracting)

Wolverine Supply Co.
Pittsburgh, Pennsylvania

Imma Whiz Games (Fundamental operations)

Kenworthy Educational Service, Inc.
Buffalo, New York

I Win (Fundamental operations)

Exclusive Playing Card Co.
Chicago, Illinois

Jack and Jill Target Game (Simple addition)

Cadaco Ellis
Merchandise Mart
Chicago, Illinois

Judy Counting Meter (Counting, sequence of numbers)

Judy Co.
Minneapolis, Minnesota

Junior Arithmetic (Fundamental operations)

Mastercraft Toy Co.
New York, New York

Kiddie Quiz (Fundamental operations)

Jacmar Manufacturing Co.
New York, New York

Lincoln Logs (Comparisons of length)

Various manufacturers.

Lionel Construction Set (Measurement)

Lionel, Inc.
New York, New York

Lotto (Number recognition, addition)

E. S. Fairchild Corp.
Rochester, New York

Magnetic Donkey Tail (Counting and adding)

Novel Novelties, Inc.
New York, New York

Magnetic Ring Toss (Fundamental operations)

Novel Novelties, Inc.
New York, New York

Make a Million (Fundamental operations, problem solving)

Parker Brothers
Salem, Massachusetts

Map Measurer (Ratio)

Malcolm's
524 North Charles Street
Baltimore, Maryland

Marble Relay (Fundamental operations)

D. T. Davis Co.
Lexington, Kentucky

Mechanical Bingo Set (Counting and adding)

Sears, Roebuck and Co.
Chicago, Illinois

Monopoly (Fundamental operations, problem solving)

Parker Brothers
Salem, Massachusetts

Number Builder (Number recognition, grouping)
Milton Bradley Co.
Springfield, Massachusetts

Number Puzzle (Number recognition, grouping)
Educational Playthings
Sandusky, Ohio

Old Maid (Number recognition, grouping)
(Use regular playing cards and Joker.)
Various manufacturers.

Optical Puzzles (Geometric shapes)
Jay-Bee Games Co.
New York, New York

Parchesi (Counting and grouping)
Various manufacturers.

Pig Dice (Number recognition, addition, multiplication)
Parker Brothers
Salem, Massachusetts

Pirate and Traveler (Counting and adding)
Milton Bradley Co.
Springfield, Massachusetts

Playway Adding Board (Counting and adding)
Educational Playthings
Sandusky, Ohio

Pocket Calculator (Fundamental operations)
Pries-Meyer Co.
Clayton, Missouri

Post Box (Geometric shapes)

Playskool Manufacturing Co.
Chicago, Illinois

Quizmo (Fundamental operations—set for addition and subtraction, another for multiplication and division)

Milton Bradley Co.
Springfield, Massachusetts

Ring Toss (Addition, multiplication)

Various manufacturers.

Rook (Number values and sequence)

Parker Brothers
Salem, Massachusetts

Rummy Royal (Addition)

Whitman Publishing Co.
Racine, Wisconsin

Skillball (Counting and adding)

Louis Marx & Co.
New York, New York

Spinner Fraction Squares (Fractions)

Creative Playthings
New York, New York

Tiddly Winks (Counting, adding, subtracting)

Various manufacturers.

Timmy Time Clock (Number sequence, reading time)

Sifo Company
St. Paul, Minnesota

Townsend Adding Board (Addition combinations)

Educational Playthings
Sandusky, Ohio

Toy Adding Machine (Addition and multiplication)

Wolverine Supply Co.
Pittsburgh, Pennsylvania

BULLETIN BOARDS

The main purpose of a bulletin board is to stimulate children to explore further the featured bulletin board theme. Consequently, any attempt to motivate children by use of a colorful bulletin board illustration must have its counterpart in supplemental activities.

It is best to keep bulletin boards confined to one particular topic or theme. Arithmetic bulletin boards, such as those illustrated here, are singular in their concept and numerical identification. By setting the stage for a particular arithmetic teaching area, bulletin boards encourage the children to "do more" about it.

Bulletin boards should be set up by the pupils. The teacher should present one or two arithmetic bulletin board themes. However, it is best to involve the pupils' thinking on subsequent bulletin board ideas. If you are teaching a topic such as addition of like fractions, why not ask the class how they would represent this on a bulletin board? Have your class break into groups, discuss the presentation of the numerical idea, and submit sketches. Then have the class choose the best idea and let the children do the bulletin boards.

Arithmetic bulletin boards should be changed frequently to correspond with the arithmetic topic being taught.

PART SIX

BULLETIN BOARDS

MUMBO JUMBO NUMBERS

CATCH THEM, COWBOY

WHO CAN GET TO THE DRIVERS SEAT FIRST

L. Costa

JANE IS 4 FT. TALL

DICK IS 4 FT. 6 INCHES TALL

THEY MUST NOT BEND

WHERE WILL JANE FIT?

WHERE WILL DICK FIT?

46 INCHES

1 YARD

60 INCHES

50 INCHES

55 INCHES

FIGURE THE ANSWERS AND SEE IF YOU ARE RIGHT BY PLACING DICK AND JANE IN EACH DRAWING

P. Thayer

M. Bowe

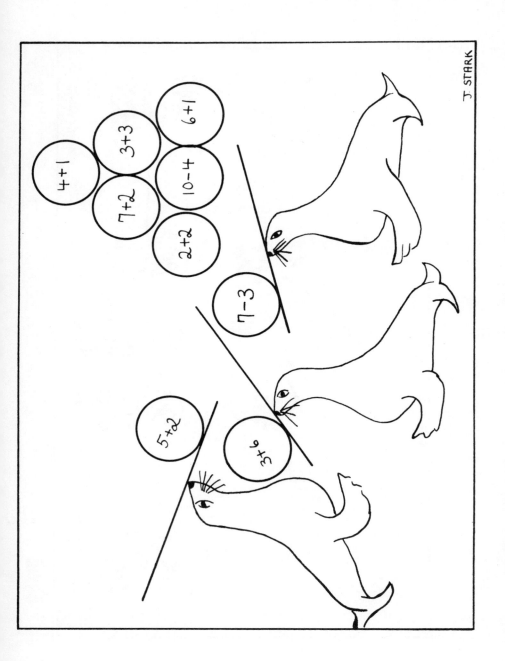

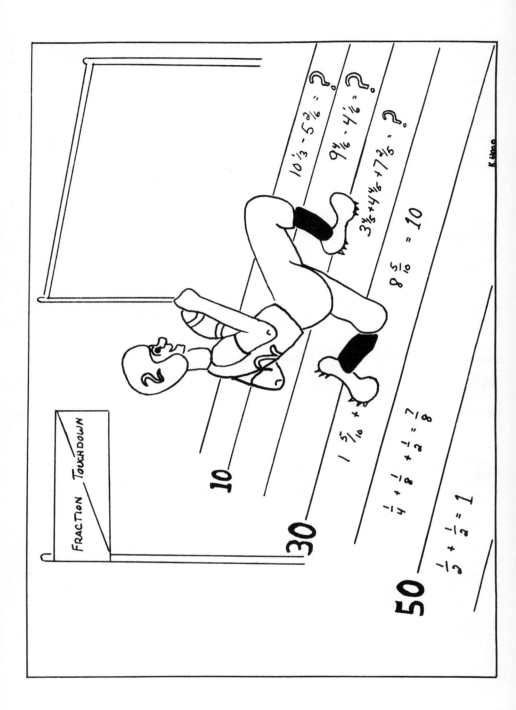

A TALE OF TIME

WHO WINS?

MR. RABBIT LEAPS
5 MIN AT A TIME

MR. TURTLE CREEPS
1 HOUR AT A TIME

MR. RABBIT SLEEPS
AT HALF PAST TIME

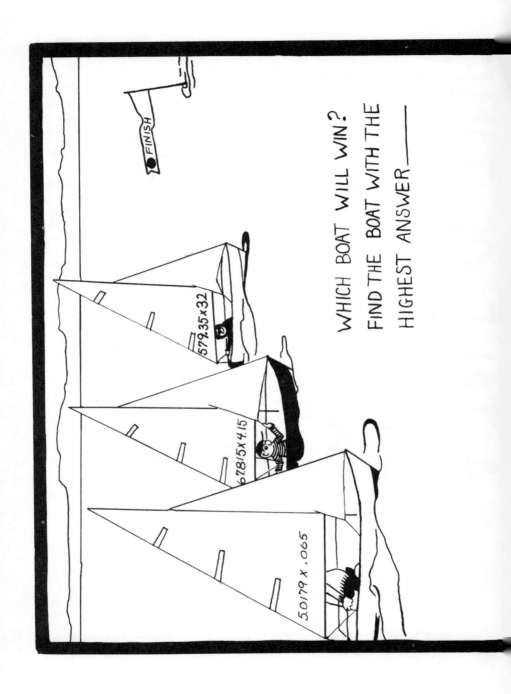

INDEX

Abacus, 41
  Arabic Number, 108–109
  Single Line Abacus, 74–75
Abbreviations, 87
Add-a-Trail, 157
Addition:
  Add-a-Trail, 157
  Addition Relay, 139–140
  As I Remember, 111
  Balance, 54
  Bean Bag, 111–112
  Beanbag Game, 76
  Bird Game, 45
  Breaking Through the Lines, 112
  Captains Compete, 147
  Cardboard Strip Reckoner, 68
  Climb the Ladder, 113
  Clothespin Counter, 52–53
  Discovering a Sum, 98
  Domino Cards, 50
  Domino Sums, 147
  Egg Box Pitch, 55
  February Picture Puzzle, 62–63
  Finding a Number, 114
  Finding Arithmetic Pairs, 89
  Gathering Acorns, 115
  Guess What It Is, 116
  Hopscotch, 116–117
  Horse Race, 117
  How Many?, 157
  Hull Gull, 117–118
  I Bought, 112
  Improved Baseball, 135
  Kitten in the Corner, 122
  Magic Addition, 30–31
  Magic Circle, 78
  Magic Rectangle, 78
  Making a Store, 49
  Making a Tree, 118
  Number Family Addition, 44
  Pairs, 121–122
  Peg Board, 53
  Puzzle Matching, 161
  Race, 57–58
  Raceway Game, 94
  Store Sales, 147–148

Addition (Cont.):
  The Twenty Stick, 68
  What Number?, 123–124
  Zooks, 124
Age:
  Guessing Your Age and House Number, 30
  I Can Guess Your Age, 32–33
  Proving Your Age, 22–23
Answer is Always the Same, 165
Answer is Always 2, 26
Arabic Number, 108–109
Arithmetic Bee, 125
Arithmetic Crossword Puzzle, 171–172
Arithmetic Tag, 129–130
Around the Circle, 134–135
Arranging or Ordering Numbers, 105
As I Remember, 111

Balance, Marble, 21–22
Balance Scale, 54
Bank For Me, 135–136
Baseball (K-2), 111
Baseball (4-6), 96–97
Baseball Game (2-3), 125
Bases, Working with Different, 180–181
Basketball, 109–110
Bean Bag, 111–112
Beanbag Game, 76
Bee, Arithmetic, 125
Bird Game, 45
Bouncing the Ball, 105
Bowling, 133
Boxes, Number, 56
Brain teasers, 19–38
  Answer is Always 2, 26
  Crossing Out to Find a Sum, 25
  Find the Squares, 35–36
  The Freight Train, 33–34
  Guessing a Number, 27
  Guessing Numbers, 26
  Guessing Your Age and House Number, 30
  Horse Trader, 31

Brain teasers (*Cont.*)
How Many Trains?, 28–29
I Can Guess Your Age, 32–33
Magic Addition, 30–31
Marble Balance, 21–22
Milk Problem, 31
Multiplying by 9, 23
A Novel Method of Multiplication, 35
Number is Always 5, 23
Number is Always 7, 25
Number is Always 9, 24
Number is Always 15, 24–25
Number is Always 10,890, 22
100 Items, 100 Cents, 29
Order of 9's, 30
Persistent Snail, 30
Proving Your Age, 22
Rapid Multiplication, 32
Reversing a Number, 24
A Riddle Poem, 27
Rules of Rapid Multiplication and Division, 37–38
Secret Code, 34–35
Three Digit Rapid Multiplication, 28
Trick Questions, 36–37
Breaking Through the Lines, 112
Bridging Numbers, 145
Bulletin boards:
flannel boards, 76, 99
purpose of, 201
set up by children, 201
Buzz-Buzz, 105–106

Call and Catch, 129
Caller, 141–142
Captains Compete, 147
Cardboard Strip Reckoner, 68
Card Matching, 72
Casting Out Nines, 169
Charts:
Double Chart, 73
Place Value Charts, 73, 99–100
pocket, 73, 99
Checkers, 125–126
Children, learning devices made by, 41
Choose a Favorite Number, 164
Christmas Stocking, 112–113
Circle of Facts, 70–71
Circle the Clock, 131
Circles:
Magic Circle, 78
Magic Wheel, 159
Number Fun With Circles, 160
Placing Numerals, 177–178
Climb the Ladder, 113

Clothespin Counter, 52–53
Combination Solitaire, 113
Codes:
A Coded Letter, 175
Number Code Puzzle, 166
Secret Code, 34–35
Secret Message, 60
Combinations of numbers:
An Arithmetic Bee, 125
Arithmetic Tag, 129–130
Bowling, 133
Call and Catch, 129
Checkers, 125–126
Christmas Stocking, 112–113
Combination Solitaire, 113
Dog and His Bone, 114
Domino Cards, 50
Finding a Number, 114
Fish Pond, 114–115
Footprints, 128–129
Fox and Geese, 115
Guess What It Is, 116
Horse Race, 117
Hull Gull, 117–118
I'm Thinking, 148
King of the Castle, 118
Ladder, 132
Larks, Robins, and Swallows, 118
Making a Tree, 118
Math-tic, 142–143
More or Less, 119
Number Combination Cards, 74
Number Family Addition, 44
Numbo, 120
Opposites and Answers, 120–121
Paper Relay, 133–134
Pony Track, 122
Race, 57–58
Racing: Two by Two, 119–120
Relay Race, 122–123
Ring Toss, 120
Sorting Mail, 123
Stepping Stones, 127–128
Step Up, 136
The Teacher, 124
Telephone, 128
Valentine Box, 123
The Whole Story, 132–133
Commercial companies, offering enrichment materials, 187–188
Commercial games, list of, 192–198
Computational deficiencies, identified by puzzles, 151
Containers, 144

Counters, 56
Counting:
　　Arranging or Ordering Numbers, 105
　　Bouncing the Ball, 105
　　Bridging Numbers, 145
　　Buzz-Buzz, 105–106
　　Clothespin Counter, 52–53
　　Flexible Hundred Board, 82–83
　　Fox and Chickens, 106
　　How Many Squares?, 69
　　I Have That Number, 106
　　Learning Odd Numbers, 69–70
　　Number Box, 56
　　Pegs, 110
　　Place Value Chart, 99
　　Seven Sequence, 59–60
　　Ten Little Indians, 110
Counting Box, 109
Counting frame, 41
Counting sticks, 56
Crossing Out to Find a Sum, 25
Crossword Puzzles, 83–84, 168
　　Arithmetic, 171–172
　　Multiplication, 166–168
　　Thinking Crossword, 172–173
Curriculum materials, 183
　　list of, 185–186

Decimals:
　　Decimal Point, 145
　　Decimal Relay, 94–95
　　Math-tic, 142–143
　　The Satellite Game, 92
Directional Puzzle, 80
Discovering a Sum, 98
Discovering Numbers (learning device), 85
Discovering Numbers (puzzle), 176
Discovering Order of Numbers, 162
Division:
　　Bowling, 133
　　Breaking Through the Lines, 112
　　Casting Out Nines, 169
　　Divide It, 137
　　Division Steps, 148
　　Division Table, 140–141
　　Guess, 146
　　Horse Race, 117
　　Race, 57–58
　　Rules for Rapid Division, 37–38
　　Simon Says, 126–127
　　Tick-Tack-Toe, 134
Dog and His Bone, 114
Domino Cards, 50

Domino Sums, 147
Double Chart, 73
Drills (see Mental arithmetic drills)

Egg Box Pitch, 55
Electrical wizard, 43–44
Enrichment aids, 9–10, 183
　　commercial companies offering, 187–188, 192–198
　　purpose of, 9–10
Estimation, 144

Factoring Practice, 126
February Picture Puzzle, 62–63
Felt figures, 76
　　used on flannel boards, 99
Fill in Missing Numbers, 158
Fill in Number, 173
Fill in the Missing Numbers, 176–177
Finding a Number, 114
Finding Arithmetic Pairs, 89
Finding the Missing Numerals, 174
Finding the Mystery Number, 165
Find the Squares, 35–36
Fish Pond, 114–115
Fish Weight, 173
Flannel boards, 76, 99
Flexible Hundred Board, 82–83
Football Game, 89–90
Footprints, 128–129
Fox and Chickens, 106
Fox and Geese, 115
Fractions:
　　Around the Circle, 134–135
　　Bowling, 133
　　Decimal Relay, 94–95
　　Football Game, 89–90
　　Fraction Change, 143
　　Guessing at Fractions, 47–48
　　Improved Baseball, 135
　　I'm Thinking, 148
　　Magic Star, 97
　　materials for teaching, 75–76
　　Recognizing Fractional Parts, 51
　　Relay Race, 149
　　Stepping Stones, 127–128
　　Why We Invert, 179–180
Freight Train, 33–34
Fruit Puzzle, 155

Games, 103–149
　　Addition Relay, 139–140
　　An Arithmetic Bee, 125
　　Arithmetic Tag, 129–130
　　Around the Circle, 134–135

Games (*Cont.*)

Arranging or Ordering Numbers, 105
As I Remember, 111
Balance, 54
Bank For Me, 135–136
Baseball (K-2), 111
Baseball (4-6), 96–97
Baseball Game (2-3), 125
Basketball, 109–110
Bean Bag, 111–112
Beanbag Game, 76
Bouncing the Ball, 105
Bowling, 133
Breaking Through the Lines, 112
Bridging Numbers, 145
Buzz-Buzz, 105–106
Call and Catch, 129
Caller, 141–142
Captains Compete, 147
Card Matching, 72
Checkers, 125–126
Christmas Stocking, 112–113
Circle the Clock, 131
Climb the Ladder, 113
Combination Solitaire, 113
commercial, 183, 192–198
Containers, 144
Decimal Point, 145
Divide It, 137
Division Steps, 148
Division Tables, 140–141
Dog and His Bone, 114
Domino Sums, 147
Egg Box Pitch, 55
Estimation, 144
Factoring Practice, 126
file of, 104
Finding a Number, 114
Fish Pond, 114–115
Footprints, 128–129
Fox and Chickens, 106
Fox and Geese, 115
Fraction Change, 143
Fraction Relay Race, 149
Gathering Acorns, 115
Golf, 137
Guess, 146
Guess What I Am, 131–132
Guess What It Is, 116
Hide and Say, 116
Hopscotch, 116–117
Horse Race, 117
How Much?, 137–138
Hull Gull, 117–118
I Bought, 112
I Can Match That Number, 106

Games (*Cont.*)

I Have That Number, 106
Improved Baseball, 135
I'm Thinking, 148
King of the Castle, 118
Kitten in the Corner, 122
Ladder, 132
Larks, Robins, and Swallows, 118
Learning Terms, 86–87
Lotto (K-2), 107
Lotto (2-4), 71–72
Making a Tree, 118
Matho, 64–65
Math-tic, 142–143
Measure in Place, 144
Measurement Equivalents, 79
More or Less, 119
Multiplication Relay, 136
Number Guessing Game, 107–108
Numberland Game, 88
number of students involved, 103–104
Number Party, 109
Numbo, 120
Opposites and Answers, 120–121
Pairs, 121–122
Paper Relay, 133–134
Pegs, 110
Pony Track, 122
Postman, 108
Race, 57–58
Raceway Game, 94
Racing: Two by Two, 119–120
Relay Race, 122–123
Ring Toss, 120
role of, 103
Ruler Relay, 130–131
Satellite Game, 92
Scramble, 109
Seven Sequence, 59–60
Silent Multiplication, 127
Simon Says, 126–127
Sorting Mail, 123
sources of new games, 104
Stepping Stones, 127–128
Step Up, 136
Store Sales, 147–148
stored in containers, 104
Teacher, The, 124
Teams, selecting, 145–146
Telephone, 128
Television Quiz Show, 138–139
Ten Little Indians, 110
Tens and Ones, 108
Tick-Tack-Toe, 134

Games (*Cont.*)
Time Around the World, 139
The Train, 110
The Traveler, 134
Twenty Questions, 128
Using the Number Line, 86
Valentine Box, 123
What Number?, 123–124
Wheel Game, 85
The Whole Story, 132–133
Zooks, 124
Gathering Acorns, 115
Golf, 137
Grouping, Peg Board, 53
Guess, 146
Guessing a number, 27
Guessing at Fractions, 47–48
Guessing Numbers, 26
Guessing Your Age and House Number, 30
Guess What I Am, 131–132
Guess What It Is, 116

Hidden Animal, The, 153
Hide and Say, 116
Hopscotch, 116–117
Horse Race, 117
Horse Trader, 31
How Many Squares?, 69
How Many Trains?, 28–29
How Much?, 137–138
Hull Gull, 117–118
Hundred Board, 82–83

I Bought, 112
I Can Guess Your Age, 32–33
I Can Match That Number, 106
I Can Read Your Mind, 165
I Have That Number, 106
Illustration Board, 61
Improved Baseball, 135
I'm Thinking, 148
I'm Thinking Again, 93
In Round Figures, 60
Instructional materials, 9

King of the Castle, 118
Kitten in the Corner, 122

Ladder, 132
Ladder Game, 78
Larks, Robins, and Swallows, 118
Lattice Multiplication, 95
Leaf Game, 65
Learning devices, 41–100
Abbreviations, 87
Adjustable Thermometer, 81–82
Balance, 54

Learning devices (*Cont.*)
Baseball, 96–97
Beanbag Game, 76
Cardboard Strip Reckoner, 68
Card Matching, 72
Circle of Facts, 70–71
Clothespin Counter, 52–53
Crossword Puzzles, 83–84
Decimal Relay, 94–95
Directional Puzzle, 80
Discovering a Sum, 98
Discovering Numbers, 85
Domino Cards, 50
Double Chart, 73
Egg Box Pitch, 55
Electrical Wizard, 43–44
February Picture Puzzle, 62–63
Finding Arithmetic Pairs, 89
Flannel Board, 99
Flexible Hundred Board, 82–83
Football Game, 89–90
Guessing at Fractions, 47–48
How Many Squares?, 69
Illustration Board, 61
I'm Thinking Again, 93
In Round Figures, 60
Ladder Game, 78
Lattice Multiplication, 95
Leaf Game, 65
Learning Odd Numbers, 69–70
Learning Terms, 86–87
Lotto, 71–72
made by children, 41
Magic Circle, 78
Magic Rectangle, 78
Magic Star, 97
Making a Slide Rule, 65–67
Making a Store, 49
Map Treasure Hunt, 90–91
materials for teaching fractions, 75–76
Matho, 64–65
Measurement Equivalents, 79
Missing Fact Cards, 70
Number Box, 56
Number Combination Cards, 74
Number Family Addition, 44
Numberland Game, 88
Peg Board, 53
Place Value Chart, 41, 73, 99–100
Playing Fireman, 77–78
purpose of, 41
Race, 57–58
Raceway Game, 94
Recognizing Fractional Parts, 51
Same Sum Number, 58–59
Satellite Game, 92

Learning devices (*Cont.*)
  Secret Message, 60
  Seven Sequence, 59–60
  Single Line Abacus, 74–75
  The Bird Game, 45
  to stimulate attitude of inquiry,
    41
  stored in envelopes, 41
  Surprise Dots, 47
  Take a Number, 47
  for teaching arithmetical con-
    cepts, 41
  Treasure Hunt, 80
  The Twenty Stick, 68
  Upside-down Magic Square, 93–
    94
  Using the Number Line, 86
  Wheel Game, 85
  Wheel Multiplication, 65
Learning Odd Numbers, 69–70
Lotto (K-2), 107
Lotto (2-4), 71–72

Magic Addition, 30–31
Magic Circle, 78
Magic Rectangle, 78
Magic Squares, 163
Magic Star (learning device), 97
Magic Star (puzzle), 159
Magic Wheel, 159
Making a Store, 49
Making a Tree, 118
Map Treasure Hunt, 90–91
Marble Balance, 21–22
Matching Cards, 107
Materials, educational, 183
  commercial companies offering,
    187–188
  list of, 185–186
Matho, 64–65
Math-tic, 142–143
Measurements:
  Containers, 144
  Estimation, 144
  Guess What I Am, 131–132
  How Much?, 137–138
  Measure in Place, 144
  Measurements (puzzle), 158
  Ruler Relay, 130–131
Measurement units:
  Abbreviations, 87
  Equivalents for, 79
Mental Arithmetic, 158
Mental arithmetic drills:
  Arithmetic Tag, 129–130
  I Bought, 112
  Missing Fact Cards, 70
Milk Problem, 31

Missing Fact Cards, 70
Money Problems, 56
  Making a Store, 49
More or Less, 119
Motivation:
  bulletin boards, 201
  enrichment aids, 9–10, 183
Multiplication:
  Bowling, 133
  Breaking Through the Lines,
    112
  Call and Catch, 129
  Caller, 141–142
  Circle the Clock, 131
  Crossword Puzzle, 166–168
  Guess, 146
  Horse Race, 117
  Illustration Board, 61
  Lattice Multiplication, 95
  Matho, 64–65
  Multiplication Relay, 136
  Novel Method of Multiplication,
    35
  Race, 57–58
  Rapid Multiplication, 32
  Rules for Rapid Multiplication,
    37–38
  Silent Multiplication, 12
  Strange Patterns in Multiplica-
    tion, 170
  Teams, selecting, 145–146
  Three Digit Rapid, 28
  Tick-Tack-Toe, 134
  The Traveler, 134
  Treasure Hunt, 80
  Wheel, 65
Multiplying by 9, 23
Mystery boxes, 56

New math programs, sources of in-
    formation about, 191–192
Nines:
  Casting Out Nines, 169
  The Funny 9, 164
  Multiplying by 9, 23
  Number is Always 9, 24
  Order of 9's, 30
  Strange Patterns in Multiplica-
    tion, 170
Novel Method of Multiplication,
    35
Number Boxes, 56
Number Code Puzzle, 166
Number Combination Cards, 74
Number Family Addition, 44
Number Fun With Circles, 160
Number Guessing Game, 107–108
Number is always 5, 23

Number is Always 7, 25
Number is Always 9, 24
Number is Always 15, 24–25
Number is Always 10,890, 22
Numberland Game, 88
Number line, 41
Number Party, 109
Number recognition:
  Card Matching, 72
  Electrical Wizard, 43–44
  February Picture Puzzle, 62–63
  Take a Number, 47
Numbers:
  Arabic Number, 108–109
  Arranging or Ordering Numbers, 105
  Basketball, 109–110
  cardinal, 47
  Card Matching, 72
  Choose a Favorite Number, 164
  combinations (*see* Combinations of numbers)
  Discovering Numbers, 85
  Discovering Order of Numbers, 162
  Find the Mystery Number, 165
  I Can Match That Number, 106
  I Have That Number, 106
  Lotto, 107
  matching:
    Christmas Stocking, 112–113
    I Can Match That Number, 106
    Lotto, 107
    Matching Cards, 107
    Postman, 108
  Matching Cards, 107
  method of reviewing basic number facts, 96–97
  Number Guessing Game, 107–108
  Numberland Game, 88
  Number Party, 109
  Pegs, 110
  Postman, 108
  Puzzle Matching Numbers, 174
  Scramble, 109
  Tens and Ones, 108
  The Train, 110
  Using the Number Line, 86
Numbo, 120

Octopus, 156
Odd Numbers, 69–70
100 Items, 100 Cents, 29
Ones, Products of One, 171
Opposites and Answers, 120–121
Order of 9's, 30

Pairs, 121–122
  Finding Arithmetic Pairs, 89
Paper Relay, 133–134
Parents, involvement in arithmetical learnings, 19
Peg Boards, 53
Pegs, 110
Percentage problems, Math-tic, 142–143
Persistent Snail, 30
Place-value box, 109
Place value chart, 41, 73, 99–100
  construction, 99
Placing Numerals, 177–178
Playing Fireman, 77–78
Play material, 56
Pocket charts, 73, 99
Pony Track, 122
Postman, 108
Problem solving:
  Baseball, 111
  Baseball Game, 125
  Golf, 137
  Lotto, 71–72
  Step Up, 136
  Television Quiz Show, 138–139
  Wheel Game, 85
Products of One, 171
Proving Your Age, 22–23
Publications:
  containing practical teaching aids and articles, 189–191
  list of free arithmetic, 188–189
Puzzles, 151–181
  Add-a-Trail, 157
  The Answer Is Always the Same, 165
  Arithmetic Crossword Puzzle, 171–172
  Casting Out Nines, 169
  Choose a Favorite Number, 164
  A Coded Letter, 175
  Crossword, 83–84
  Crossword Puzzle, 168
  to develop thinking powers, 151
  Directional Puzzle, 80
  Discovering Numbers, 176
  Discovering Order of Numbers, 162
  for enrichment, 151
  February Picture Puzzle, 62–63
  Fill in Missing Numbers, 158
  Fill in Number, 173
  Fill in the Missing Numbers, 176–177
  Finding the Missing Numerals, 174
  Find the Mystery Number, 165

Puzzles (*Cont.*)
  Fish Weight, 173
  Fruit Puzzle, 155
  The Funny 9, 164
  The Hidden Animal, 153
  How Many?, 157
  I Can Read Your Mind, 165
  to identify computational deficiencies, 151
  jig-saw, for teaching fractions, 75–76
  Magic Squares, 163
  Magic Star, 159
  Magic Wheel, 159
  Measurements, 158
  Mental Arithmetic, 158
  Multiplication Crossword Puzzle, 166–168
  Number Code Puzzle, 166
  Number Fun With Circles, 160
  objectives, 151
  Octopus, 156
  Placing Numerals, 177–178
  Products of One, 171
  Puzzle Matching, 161
  Puzzle Matching Numbers, 174
  Same Sum Number, 58–59
  Secret Message, 60
  Strange Patterns in Multiplication, 170
  Surprise, A, 169
  Thinking Crossword, 172–173
  What Comes Next?, 154
  Why We Invert, 179–180
  Working with Different Bases, 180–181
  Working with 8's, 170
  Working with 4's, 171

Questions:
  Trick Questions, 36–37
  Twenty Questions, 128

Race, 57–58
Raceway Game, 94
Racing: Two by Two, 119–120
Rapid Multiplication, 32
Recognizing Fractional Parts, 51
Rectangles, Magic, 78
Relay Race, 122–123
Reversing a Number, 24
Riddles, 27
  Trick Questions, 36–37
Ring Toss, 120
Roman Numerals:
  I Can Match That Number, 106
Ruler Relay, 130–131

Rules for Rapid Multiplication and Division, 37–38

Same Sum Number, 58–59
Satellite Game, 92
Scramble, 109
Secret Code, 34–35
Secret Message, 60
Sensory aids, 9–10
Seven Sequence, 59–60
Silent Multiplication, 127
Simon Says, 126–127
Slide Rule, making, 65–67
Sorting Mail, 123
Squares:
  Find the Squares, 35–36
  How Many Squares?, 69
  Upside-down Magic Square, 93–94
Stepping Stones, 127–128
Step Up, 136
Stores, play, 49
Store Sales, 147–148
Subtraction:
  As I Remember, 111
  Balance, 54
  Bean Bag, 111–112
  Breaking Through the Lines, 112
  Cardboard Strip Reckoner, 68
  Climb the Ladder, 113
  Clothespin Counter, 52–53
  Domino Cards, 50
  February Picture Puzzle, 62–63
  Gathering Acorns, 115
  Hide and Say, 116
  Hopscotch, 116–117
  Horse Race, 117
  Hull Gull, 117–118
  I Bought, 112
  Improved Baseball, 135
  Making a Tree, 118
  Peg Boards, 53
  Race, 57–58
  Raceway Game, 94
  The Twenty Stick, 68
  Zooks, 124
Surprise, A (puzzle), 169
Surprise Dots, 47

Take a Number, 47
Teacher, The, 124
Teams, selecting, 145–146
Telephone, 128
Television Quiz Show, 138–139
Ten Little Indians, 110
Tens and Ones, 108
Terms, arithmetic, 86–87

Thermometers, Adjustable, 81–82
Thinking Crossword, 172–173
Thinking power, puzzles used to develop, 151
Three Digit Rapid Multiplication, 28
Tick-Tack-Toe, 134
Time Around the World, 139
Tongue depressers, used for counters, 56
Traveler, The, 134
Treasure Hunt, 80
Trick Questions, 36–37
Twenty Questions, 128
Twenty Stick, 68

Upside-down Magic Square, 93–94

Using the Number Line, 86

Valentine Box, 123

What Comes Next?, 154
What Number?, 123–124
Wheel Game, 85
Wheel Multiplication, 65
Whole Story, The, 132–133
Why We Invert, 179–180
Working with Different Bases, 180–181
Working with 8's, 170
Working with 4's, 171

Zero, teaching the meaning of, 76
Zooks, 124